Published in Great Britain by
L.R. Price Publications Ltd., 2022.
27 Old Gloucester Street,
London,
WC1N 3AX
www.lrpricepublications.com

Cover artwork by Janelle Hope

Photographs courtesey of Katie Herdman

ISBN-13: 9781915330208

This book is dedicated to my husband
WITH IMMENSE LOVE.

E' un petalo la tua memoria che si
adagia sul cuore e lo sconvolge
by Alda Merini.

Your memory is a petal that touches
my heart and shatters it.

Where Are You?

Katie Herdman

"That is great, Jim."

Yesterday was a good day. We went to London, you and me, our son Adri and his wife Truc. We walked onto Waterloo Bridge, where the environmental protesters were. And it felt good. It was a sunny day. You held on to my hand all the way from Waterloo Station to the restaurant in St Martin's Lane.

Thursday 9th May 2019

After your mental collapse and hospitalisation back in March, you changed significantly, almost overnight. You had been slowly deteriorating over the previous few months, but you were still 'my Jim'. Yes, you forgot the odd word here and there. And yes, you walked slowly and at times you slumped forward. But it was still you. My love, my funny, kind, sensual man. At the beginning of March I had to call an ambulance because you were delirious and paranoid. Unfortunately, during your stay in hospital you became even more paranoid. Once you were discharged you were greatly diminished and I had to accept that you could no longer be left on your own. Adri and I started the search for a part-time private carer who could be with you whilst we were at work.

Today was meant to be the second day of trialling the three carers we shortlisted. We got up at the normal time, after a decent night's sleep. I had taken the week off to explain your routine and habits to the carers and had planned to leave the house to allow time for the two of you to get used to each other. I planned to return to the house at 3.00 p.m. at the end of the carer's shift. The first carer to be trialled was Cece, who came here yesterday. Unfortunately, that was not a success. You rang me four times between twelve noon and 2.00 p.m. So I decided I should come home, as you were complaining that the door was locked and you could not get out. When I arrived home,

Cece explained that when you got back from your walk at approximately 11.15 a.m., she started cooking your lunch but you said you wanted to go for another walk. Cece obviously told you that you had just come back from a walk and you needed to eat. She then locked the front door whilst she prepared your lunch in the kitchen and this set you off. You detest the feeling of not being able to 'run away' if necessary. You have always treasured your freedom and are not prepared to give it up just because you are unwell. Cece did not know this, but that was the worst thing she could have done to you.

Back to this morning, we were having breakfast at 10.00 a.m. when the doorbell rang. It was Michelle from CRS coming to measure up for a grab-rail to put between the two front doors, which will make it easier for you to get out. I answered the door and you also left the table to join us. Somehow, you must have misunderstood the purpose of Michelle's visit, as you became very agitated. Anyhow, Michelle measured up and left and you said you were going out. I said we had to wait for the second carer, who was due to arrive at 11.00 a.m., but you would not listen. I held on to your arm in an attempt to stop you from leaving, but I should have known better by now. You grabbed my scarf to get me out of the way and for a moment I felt constricted. You would never hurt me intentionally; I know that for sure. Moreover, you are very weak now and I can push you away easily. I tend not do it, however, as your balance is a bit precarious and you may fall if I push you away. You let go of my scarf as soon as you realised what was happening and I, in turn, let go of you. When you opened the inside front door I noticed that Michelle was still sitting in her car at the front of the house. I called her and said I needed help. She came back in and managed to calm you down and you decided to remain at home and wait for the second carer to arrive. Michelle also managed to arrange an emergency appointment with the doctor in order to speed up the psychiatric assessment that Dr Tai, your neurologist, had mentioned to us two weeks earlier.

We visited the doctor, who said he would try to have someone contact us the following week. Driving home from the surgery you apologised and said you wished all this had never happened. I was too upset and too distressed to appease you and could not bring myself to be kind to you: the man I love so much; the man I have been so happy with for almost forty years. It is all so tragic. I now dread weekends, bank holidays and holidays. I used to love them as I knew there would be excitement and fun in store with you. Yes, at times there was heartache, even then. For example, when you got drunk and would then feel guilty and isolate yourself. And there were your portentous rages, which were scary, even though you were never violent. But most of the time we were great and happy together. With you, life was never boring. You always found a way to bring some excitement everywhere, on every occasion.

You loved mental puzzles, quizzes, crosswords and words in general. You liked saying a word, then adding as many synonyms as you could think of. And reading. You loved reading. Your Guardian newspaper and books. You were an avid reader and could get completely absorbed in a story for hours on end.

You taught me all I know about authors and books. Although I read before I met you, the range of your knowledge was much greater than mine. You introduced me to Graham Green and to his connection with 'Rules', our favourite restaurant because of that connection. You talked to me about John Updike, Tom Sharpe, Albert Camus, Iris Murdoch, Fay Weldon, Alison Lurie, Gore Vidal and so many others. You read the reviews and then advised me on the best books to read, shows to see, exhibitions to attend. How influential you have been in my life.

You never bought me flowers. I used to ask you to buy them as a romantic gesture, but you always felt too awkward to carry a bunch of flowers. However, books and music you bought me in abundance. There was no need for an anniversary or a birthday for you to buy me books. If you saw a book you thought I would enjoy, you would buy it for me and you would write a loving inscription inside the book. How I loved those gifts as they confirmed your love for me, and I shall always treasure them.

Friday 31st May 2019

12.45 p.m.: I am working from home. You really should have gone for your walk, but you wanted to wait because you felt you needed the toilet. On entering the toilet you asked, "What do I do next?"

I replied, "Lower your trousers below your knees."

"Oh yes," you said, as you sat down on the toilet and strained to have a poo. "What happens next?"

"If you are finished, stand up and clean yourself."

"Don't shout at me," you said.

"I'm not shouting, I'm just emphasising my words." I replied. I could see by looking in the bowl that you had done neither a pee nor a poo. You then pulled your trousers up, and I said, "Now flush and wash your hands." We walked downstairs and again you asked,

"What happens next?"

"Go for a walk," I replied. And this is the level of exchange I have with my husband, who was one of the smartest, wittiest, most eloquent people I knew. How am I going to go on like this? Adri has shortlisted some counsellors for me to talk to. As he can see, I am not coping. Jim, this version of you is killing all the good memories, the happy years we had together. I feel so sorry for you and for me and hate what you have become and myself for not being able to accept this.

The only thing that is still good is the sex. Your increased sexual activity, I believe, is caused by the Parkinson's medications. You feel like having sex quite regularly; two, three times a week. For a man who will be eighty next week this is quite impressive! Sex is reciprocal caressing and mutual masturbation, as nothing else would be possible for you now. At times I sit on your face and this adds a spark to our sex life. I still get excited very quickly when you touch me. When you caress my nipples, stroke my thighs and start stimulating my clitoris. Usually I come within a few minutes and it feels so good that I almost forget our new reality. You also come fast and at times you come without ejaculating. This, we read can happen. You even said that when you do not ejaculate the orgasm seems more intense. Sexually, you have always been an exciting and creative lover. You used to tell me to 'fuck the wall' when you were penetrating me from behind, standing up. I would then wobble towards the wall, releasing your cock from inside me and I would touch myself whilst 'fucking' the wall. This used to excite you and you would walk towards me, touch my arse and make yourself come. The 'fucking the wall' is also a scene in 'The Unbearable Lightness of Being', but you started this practice well before we read the book or saw the film. I love both the book and the film, and this connection makes them special to me.

Saturday 27th July 2019

1.15 p.m.: You have just returned from your walk. You said that you went to the pub for a glass of wine. You could hardly walk up the path leading to the house when you arrived back and I had to come out to help you. You walked in looking as though you do not know anything about anything. I wonder whether this could have been caused by yet another row that we had as soon as we got up yesterday. As it was Friday, I was working from home. When I got up, I checked my emails, rang the doctor about your prescriptions and then showered and went back to my laptop. At approximately 9.30 a.m. you woke up. I went upstairs to help you into the shower and to wash your hair. After doing so, I closed the shower's partition to allow you to wash yourself. In so doing, I must have touched your backside, because you reacted as though I had hit you with an iron bar. In turn, I responded by displaying resentment, as I often do when you overreact, and you asked me to leave you alone. I went downstairs, knowing full-well that I needed to go back up to help you dry yourself and get dressed. Ten minutes later, you had finished showering so I went back upstairs and reminded you to brush your teeth. You asked why and I replied, "Because they are full of shit." You resented this but relented and brushed your teeth. However, you did not rinse your mouth properly and still had some toothpaste on your lips. I asked you to rinse again and you swore at me.

the floor. You then accused me of hitting you. I petulantly replied that I just touched the back of your knee against the leg of the table. Now we are back where we started: arguing again.

Friday 6th September 2019

It is a Friday and, as usual, I'm working from home in order to be with you. We came back from holiday on Wednesday and I found my return to the office to be very sad. My line manager, Chris, who I've worked with for nineteen years has gone and the team has been disbanded. Chris had called me while we were in Italy to let me know what was happening and since returning, I've been supporting the senior team as well as other colleagues. All in all, it's been a very stressful working week. On top of this, you have been very bad, both in terms of behaviour and physically. It all started in Italy during our holiday, when your paranoia returned as strong as when I first called the ambulance back in March. Up to that point, we had not had any further incidents like that. You believed that you were being held in Italy against your will and kept saying that if you had the money, you would fly back home to England. I explained that we had booked our flights to go back on 3rd September and that buying additional tickets to fly home earlier would have been costly and unfair to me.

My parents are now very old and I see them only a couple of times a year. You didn't seem to care and even Adri, who usually manages to calm you down, could not do so. It took you hours and hours to get back to normal. This happened a couple of times during the holiday. This means that we will never be able to go on holiday again. The plans we shared for our retirement - spending six months in London and six months in Italy each year - have crumbled around us and the sadness and despair I feel has no limits. I can only see a very bleak future with no hope, no respite and no light. I hate my life and I also feel guilty for not accepting my fate. However, I also understand that you are worse off because you are ill. In the moments that you realise how you have behaved I know that you feel very ashamed and embarrassed. My feelings are exacerbated by worries about work. Because my company is in the process of being acquired, I may have to leave my job sooner than I had planned or wanted. My plan was to work until September 2020, then retire and work one or two days per week as a consultant. It is, however, possible that my role will be made redundant within the next couple of months. This means that I may have to become your full-time carer, as our income would be greatly reduced and I would be unlikely to find another job at the same level or salary. I would, therefore, not be able to afford a private carer. This depresses me so much. I am looking at you, asleep on your chair with our cat, Dice, on your lap. I feel so much anguish for the person you have become: fearful, indecisive and slow physically and mentally. How has this happened to you, to me, to us? It is not fair. You tremble slightly in your sleep and I wonder what demons are clouding your mind, my love. I do still care so very much, but at times I feel such despair for this slow and painful death of our love, dreams and life together. I cannot bear it.

We went to the doctor this morning, as yesterday you did not eat, could hardly stand up and were exhausted all day. You did not even want to go for a walk to get the paper with Sabina, your carer. The doctor believes you may have a chest infection, as you also have a cold, but she prescribed antibiotics without even checking you. I do hope that the paranoia and confusion in Italy was due to an infection, but somehow I doubt it. I think this is our new reality, made up of rancour, misunderstanding, frustration and rage alongside the odd kind gestures and affection. I feel trapped, alone and frightened. There is no support from Social Services or the medical profession. They all look at you, then talk to me. And basically very little changes and I am stuck with you, without any help or respite. Adri is the only person who helps, but he has his own life and worries, with his new business and buying a new house.

You have just woken up and you are again confused. Earlier, I shouted at you because, after trying to settle you into the chair so that you could have a rest, you kept asking me to leave you alone. "I am happy not to talk to you for the rest of my life. Is that leaving you alone enough?" I retorted.

"You cannot say you love me and then say things like that," you replied. And you are right, it is a paradox. Do I love you now? I feel sorry for you. I pity you. And I do not wish you any harm. But do I love you? Oh, I do love you. How can I not? I know that love is still there underneath all the other negative feelings. I feel so full of resentment. Looking back at our lives together, at what we had, the loss seems unbearable. The four years we spent in Italy left an indelible mark on so many people there. You have always been the friend of the outsiders, the outcasts. But in Italy, this was much more so, as we lived in a small village where everybody knows everybody else. There was a small group of individuals living in the village who were all 'different' in some way. They were instantly attracted to you and obviously sensed that you were someone who did not see their differences and would treat them just as you would anyone else. You also made life exciting and fun at all times. You taught the village youngsters to play chess and cricket. You showed my sister, Mari, how to play backgammon, which she loves to this day. She asked you during our latest holiday to remind her of the rules of the game, but it soon transpired that it was beyond you, as sadly I knew it would be.

Where has it all gone? You were not just clever; you were also very knowledgeable. You seemed to know everything about everything. We used to love watching quiz programmes on TV. Mastermind was one of our favourites, during which I used to count your correct answers to the general knowledge questions - very often you answered more than the contestants!

While Adri was at university he joined a pub quiz team and at times he would ring you up to ask you about some topic he and his friends could not answer. You were so proud of this. If I found myself in a situation where there was uncertainty about something and different opinions were being offered, no matter what the subject, I used to say, 'Let me check with Jim. He will know'. And more often than not you did know and you would be able to back up your response with facts. Your knowledge was deep and varied. You were my personal 'Google'.

5:55pm: I have just come downstairs after a trip to the toilet for yet another shit you didn't need. The whole tiring procedure, which turned out to be for nothing, brought my evil streak out and I shouted and belittled you. I left you in the toilet to dress yourself and stormed down the stairs. Oh, how I hate myself for these outbursts. They seem so nasty and unfair, but I seem unable to control myself. Now you have made your way down the stairs by yourself and you are sniffing, which irritates me tremendously. "Blow your bloody nose," I say. Oh, I am such a witch and I feel terrible guilt. "Jim, I am sorry, my love. I do not mean to be so nasty." I move close to you and cover your forehead with kisses, to which you respond,

"You are so beautiful, Cath. Thanks for this."

Friday 20th September 2019

Tomorrow is my birthday and yesterday you tried to buy me a present at Pandora. Unfortunately you had forgotten your card's PIN number and after three attempts at punching it in, your card was blocked. Sabina called Adri for the pin number but it was too late, of course. The shop assistant advised, however, that they would keep the present aside, behind the counter, if you could go to the shop again today with Adri. But he has something important on at work today so can't go with you. You told me what had happened, so I have assured you that I will accompany you later on this afternoon to collect the gift. Adri also took you to the neurologist yesterday for a private consultation, as we are both very worried about you. We had to do this using private healthcare, because your NHS appointments are ten months apart and only consist of a ten minute chat with the doctor, which usually results in an increase of your tablets. It is a disgrace really that there is so little help and support. Your appointment was in the afternoon. That morning during your walk you had fallen and Adri had to come to get you. This shook you up even further, as you had never fallen before. The neurologist is a nice man, but he did not clarify or confirm anything. We are still waiting for the report on the psychiatric assessment that was carried out in July. He could not tell us when we would get it or what it revealed, apart from the fact that there are some cognitive issues. Thanks Dr Tai: tell us something we do not know!

On Monday 17th September you called me at work, just after 11.00 a.m. I was with someone at the time and as Monday is one of the days Sabina is with you from 11.00 a.m., I did not pick up the phone. Later on, I saw I had a voicemail from you. Whilst you were calling me, Sabina must have walked into the house and I heard you say to her, "What have I done wrong? I have been waiting for you for an hour." Sabina replied,

"Jim, I start at 11.00 a.m." Then the phone went dead. I felt so much tenderness and pity for you, my love. So lost and afraid. Unable to communicate properly and losing your grasp on reality. I switch between feeling sorry for myself to feeling ashamed for shouting at you and for being so mean. Our plans on my retirement to spend summer in Italy and winter in London, for the cultural scene, are truly dead. I see us staying in London, but not going further than the surroundings of our home. Cinema might be the only cultural activity that we are able to undertake. Your beautiful, sharp mind is wrapped in a black, woollen cloth, which scrambles the world around you. As films still stir some emotions in you we go to the cinema quite regularly. You used to be a film buff and I remember how you and Adri would frequently discuss films, actors and directors. The week before you underwent bypass surgery in 1995, we had watched 'The River Wild'. There is a scene in the film where Meryl Streep raises her thumb, index and little fingers to show her husband that she loves him. We liked this symbolism. When they brought you back from the theatre you were barely awake and full of tubes and drips, but you raised your hand and made the same sign with your fingers as Meryl Streep had. I could have melted with love for you. I also loved 'The Last of the Mohicans'. Knowing this, you would often proclaim, in a Daniel Day Lewis tone, "Stay alive, no matter what occurs. I will find you." You loved all kinds of 'good' films: redemption films like 'On the Waterfront' and 'In Bruges' and those that stirred pure unadulterated emotions, such as 'Chariots of Fire', 'Schindler's List' and 'Shane'. But you also loved all of Ken Loach's films on social inequalities. I believe that films gave you an opportunity, more than any other medium, to be in the moment and forget about anything else. You loved a good story, music and scenography as in 'Cabaret', which was one of your all-time favourites. It is not unusual for us to visit the cinema once a week. Even when the general feeling was that cinema was dead because of the inception of videos, we kept going and are still doing so, even now. We shared a love for the whole cinema experience. We would always buy a glass of wine if we were at the Curzon in Richmond, or a pack of Maltesers when elsewhere. We loved the trailers and the darkness of the cinema, which for us created an intimate, cosy world where we could shut off everything and get lost in the story. Certain scenes would make you cry. Initially you hid your tears from me, but once you realised that I also cried you would allow them to flow. We both loved this very private time together, sharing tissues, chocolate, tears and, very often, laughter.

What am I going to do? Retire and look after you full-time? Or get another job once DSV lets me go (which I fear will be very soon) and increase the days/hours of the carer? I do not know. How I was looking forward to spending all my time with you, but now everything has changed. The good news is that you have started going to the toilet unassisted again. This could simply be because we had a disabled toilet with handles installed whilst we were on holiday. I am not sure, but surely this is positive? I don't know what triggered this anxiety and, in turn, inability to go to the toilet unassisted in the first place. I know, however, that it started a couple of weeks after you were discharged from hospital in March, but why I am not sure. Even when you were in hospital, totally delirious and completely manic, you could get to the toilet by yourself. The medical staff gave you sedatives at the time, against our advice, to calm you down and send you to sleep. They also put a pad on you to avoid accidents. As soon as the sedative wore off, approximately one hour after administered, you tore the nappy off and went to the toilet by yourself, while I held on to your arm, as you were very weak.

Saturday 28 September 2019

10.00 p.m.: We are in West Middlesex Hospital. Adri and his wife Truc have just left and I am here to spend the night with you. The last six hours have been horrific. You were aggressive, agitated, confused and very, very unwell. At 3.40 a.m. you woke up and started your usual routine of climbing in and out of bed. Your chest made a terrible noise every time you took a breath and you had a bad cold. At 6.15 a.m. I administered your morning tablets as normal; these usually send you back to sleep for another few hours. You fell asleep at approximately 7.00 a.m. and woke up again two hours later, very unsettled and confused. I tried to take you for a shower, but to get you out of bed and standing straight became a major enterprise. We managed to make it back to the bedroom eventually. However, I could not dress you, because you were unable to remain standing. I needed to call Adri to help get you dressed and down the stairs. I knew that there must be something majorly wrong with you. What you said made no sense whatsoever, such as, "My word paper has moved and turn the eggs over." You do, at times, get confused and talk out of turn, but usually you realise it straight away and correct yourself. This morning, however, you were unable to make any connections. You felt very hot to the touch and were unable to stand or take a step.

Adri and I decided to call an ambulance, fearing that you might have another infection. On the way to the hospital, I promised you that we would get you back home the same day, as when you were in hospital back in March, you felt that you were being held prisoner. You believed you had been interned without your consent. Because of that, I felt that I had to discharge you after three days, before a full assessment was carried out. Your mental state was degenerating fast, so I thought it would be better to get you out. I could not keep my promise, however, as all the doctors informed us that you needed to be treated for the infection in the hospital. They also overruled your protests to be discharged, stating that you were not capable of making your own decisions and that you should remain in hospital where they could treat you. Reluctantly, both Adri and I agreed with the doctors. We felt that we had no alternative, because you are so physically incapacitated that I cannot possibly look after you at home. Your aggression towards doctors, nurses, myself and, at times, even Adri is absolutely horrific. This is a new, worrying development in your illness. On top of this, witnessing the strength you are able to muster is also frightening, as these days you are usually so frail and weak. I look at you now and you are still so restless, pulling at your clothes and talking nonsense to yourself. It has been almost seven hours since they gave you some sort of tranquilliser, which obviously went to your head, just as I told the doctor and nurses that it would. As this had happened before, I flagged it to all the medical staff treating you, but they believed that it was going to be all right. It obviously wasn't. You will never come back to me as you were, I know that. But I really hope that you can overcome this crisis, because I could not manage to take care of you at home the way you are now. You would require twenty-four hour professional care, which I would be unable to provide.

Sunday 29 September 2019

9.40 p.m.: We are still in hospital. You are now resting. After all the aggression and the thrashing around, I am not surprised. This spell of illness/hospitalisation has brought out an aggressive and violent side that you very seldom displayed until now. Yes, there have been moments of aggression, but they were very short lived and because of your weakness and your lack of intention to hit or hurt anybody, they have never been really scary. This time around, however, you seem to have gained a strength and I am not sure where it's coming from. I can only surmise that it is driven by adrenaline, which gives you this extra power and energy. The latest episode happened when you got out of bed to go to the toilet. As you are still very shaky on your legs, a nurse came to assist me. The unfortunate thing was that it was a male nurse, and this made you frantic. You started shouting, "Police, po-lice," and kept lashing out at him. When he called another nurse to come and help - another male nurse - you became hysterical. I can only assume that you felt you were going to be attacked, as you kept calling out for the police. Your hitting out was probably a means of defending yourself. The nurses then left as you said you did not need to go to the toilet after all. The first nurse looked at me with great sadness and asked me how I coped at home. I told him that this is not your normal behaviour. But I am so afraid that this 'you' may be the new norm. It has been two days now, with no behavioural improvement, despite your temperature having subsided and the infection having been brought under control. Should this be the case, I could not and would not look after you and I would have no option but to seek an alternative. A care home would be the last resort, of course. I do not want to do that to you - it would break my heart. This afternoon, while talking to Adri and me, you started crying and asked us if we would visit you regularly. You obviously thought you were in a care home. Later on, you even thought that you were in prison. When I left the hospital to go home, change and grab a few hours' sleep while Adri stayed with you, I cried with enormous sadness and anger for what Parkinson's has done to you; to my beautiful, interesting, sexy and kind husband. No one has confirmed to us that you have dementia, or indeed given us any medication for it, so I presume that all these symptoms are caused by Parkinson's. What an awful illness. How terrible it can be, I am not sure is well known. As Adri says, Parkinson's has taken everything from you: speech, thought process, charm, wit and humanity. I remember that when you were first diagnosed, I was so pleased that it was not Alzheimer's. Now I am not so sure. At least with dementia, 'in the moment' you would be the same person we love, instead of this stranger who has taken over your body and mind.

Adri and Truc are exceptionally good with you. They remain calm, patient and understanding, while I cannot help losing my temper every time you become aggressive or are totally unreasonable.

Monday 30th September 2019

6.00 p.m: I left the hospital a couple of hours ago and have not stopped sobbing since. Last night was sheer hell. You would not settle and kept talking to yourself, staring up at the ceiling in terror. Goodness knows what type of monsters you saw. You kept raising your hands towards the ceiling, taking hold of some invisible thread that you then twisted and discarded. You kept trying to get out of bed, but I knew you were unable to stand or walk alone and this meant that you would have needed to be lifted back into bed. I cannot do that by myself and I was reluctant to ask the nurses for help, as the only two on duty were the same nurses who first triggered your panic attack. I hate to admit this, but I also feel that it may be black, male nurses who set you off. Whatever deep seated prejudice you may have obviously comes out under stress.

You have always been a very inclusive and tolerant person and you have never displayed any prejudice towards anyone, so I wonder whether you may have some sort of unconscious bias that you and I are not aware of? In any case, I didn't want to disturb the nurses, as it is becoming apparent that they see you as a nuisance. They have many other patients and you do not listen to what they tell you, reacting badly to their offer of help. So in order to keep you in bed, without bothering anyone, I spent most of the night lifting your legs back onto the bed. This thrashing went on until 4.00 a.m. You then collapsed into a very restless sleep and I managed a few hours' sleep too. This morning you didn't seem too bad. Two female nurses changed your bed and gave you a wash, and you seemed okay. When the doctor came I told him that we need to get you out of the hospital as your mental state has significantly deteriorated. I also mentioned that nil by mouth, as advised by another doctor, does not help you recoup your strength. He replied that you should not be on nil by mouth and added that, providing you can keep some food down, you could go home. I fed you some lunch when it arrived as you are unable to feed yourself. I tried to give you some water but you choked on it. Your chest still sounded terrible and anything you said still did not make a lot of sense. The two health assistants advised me to keep you on the chair, rather than in bed. With great effort they helped you onto the chair and as soon as they left you tried to get up. After numerous attempts, you eventually managed to stand up but you were very wobbly. I grabbed hold of you to try to sit you back down on the bed, but you could not walk the few steps to it. So I called for assistance and a male nurse - white this time - came to help. But you were uncooperative and would not listen to him. After only a couple of minutes, the nurse stated that he had other patients to tend to and did not have all day. I then adopted an authoritarian tone and said, "Sit down Jim." This caused a violent reaction from you. You tried to hit me and the nurse, who was horrified, asked me how I cope with you. I did not reply as I knew that all he could see was this aggressive, uncooperative person. Once we got you into bed, you lay down for around half an hour and then out you climbed again. I tried to grab you but you pushed me away and fell to the floor against the bed. I called the health assistants for help. They got you back up onto your feet and suggested seating you in the chair again, but this time next to the open door onto the ward so that they could keep an eye on you. You kept trying to get up, but each time I pushed you back down onto the chair. You then said you needed a poo, so I asked for a commode. By the time it arrived you were desperate. The nurse and I tried to sit you onto the commode by transferring you from the chair. This proved very laborious, as you put up resistance and did not cooperate. Once we got you half on it you lashed out at me. We eventually sat you fully onto it. But you had a bit of diarrhoea and had already partly leaked onto the side of the commode. When you had finished I tried to stand you up to clean you, but there was shit everywhere and I struggled to hold on to you while grabbing sufficient paper to clean up. I stretched to get some more paper, which must have made you feel unsafe and you tried to hit me again. Right at that moment the nurse walked in and I burst out crying. She told me to go home and get some rest and that they would look after you. I left because I was tired and desperate. However, I do worry because your erratic, aggressive, uncooperative behaviour makes you an ideal target for abuse and neglect. I have cried all the way home. And I am still sobbing, as I do not know what to do for the best. I need help to keep you at home, but I do not think this will be available. The support, so far, has been rather poor. I feel so lost and so abandoned. Adri is now with you and sent me a text saying you are asleep.

Wednesday 2nd October 2019

4.00 p.m.: I am in your hospital room and you are asleep. It is now your fifth day in hospital and although physically you are getting better, your mind remains in turmoil. You feel betrayed by both Adri and me for our inability or unwillingness (from your perspective) to get you home. Your paranoia makes you see conspiracy theories everywhere. You also cannot grasp the fact that it is far from ideal for either Adri or me to be stuck in a hospital room, day and night, in order to keep you company to avoid you feeling even more abandoned. Unfortunately, we are in a catch 22 situation. The physiotherapist, Bethany, has offered us a six week rehab programme at home, plus a carer to help out with specific tasks on a more permanent basis. However, following Bethany's assessment, she believes, rightly, that you will not be able to walk up and down the stairs at home to go to the toilet or to bed. To ease your mental anguish, I suggested that we could get you out sooner if we had a commode to keep downstairs until you are fit again. Adri and I could get you up and down the stairs in the morning and evening, then you would be on one level for the whole day. Unfortunately, if we discharge you before everything is in place with Social Services we will no longer be within the hospital's remit and both the carer and the physio will be cancelled. Therefore, you need to remain in hospital until all the arrangements have been made. This also means that your mental state will probably deteriorate further. Bethany said that it may take forty-eight hours to arrange everything. I emphasised how this is detrimental to your mental health and urged her to try to resolve the situation by tomorrow, Thursday. It is all such a nightmare.

Wednesday 30th October 2019

You have now been out of the hospital for over three weeks. The first night home was traumatic. You didn't want to sit on the commode. Eventually, with Adri's help you made it up the stairs and used the toilet. We put the commode in the garage, as you were somehow managing to get yourself up the stairs to the toilet on your own. The week of your discharge, however, you went totally crazy with Sabina, who had been with you since April and with whom you had a good relationship. At the time, we had been unable to secure a carer from Social Services, as it would only have been for blocks of half an hour at a time. While I was at work you went out for your usual walk, telling Sabina that you did not want her to come with you. Clearly, she could not leave you alone as she is responsible for you and you have become prone to falling. She therefore followed you at a discreet distance, but you kept swearing at her, using really strong epithets. When I came home early to be with you, Sabina left, clearly feeling very upset. Unfortunately, the next day was even worse and you continued to insult Sabina. During your walk, Sabina once again followed you for your own safety. She kept updating me, saying that you were being vile and sounding really confused. I asked Adri to leave work early in order to rescue Sabina and get you home. Adri eventually managed to get you home, but you were so tired that he had to get an Uber as you could not walk all the way back. Sabina had to report these incidents to the agency, who informed us that they could not accept this behaviour and therefore could not provide the service any longer. I panicked as I am in the process of negotiating my exit from Panalpina, following the DSV takeover, and cannot yet be at home to look after you. So I rang the social worker who was involved in your discharge from the hospital and she provided names of other care agencies that could help. One agency responded immediately and within a couple of days a new private carer was in situ for the same three days a week as before, but for slightly longer periods. Harrie, your new carer, was made aware of the possibility of you becoming irate and insulting. Thankfully, she said that she would be able to handle everything you throw at her. She seems really nice. She looks very strong and seems to care. In the meantime, your moods and level of activities have been up and down. We went to London on Saturday to see the Lucian Freud exhibition. You were okay overall, despite not appearing to be very interested in the paintings. And you walked rather well. On Monday, Harrie sent me a message saying you were in a good mood and went for a long walk. Yesterday, the situation was totally reversed and Harrie said you were incapable of taking even a step. You did not go out at all. And you did not do any exercises at home either. Harrie said you slept on and off all day. When I came home you seemed to have perked up a bit. Last night you had a good night's sleep but this morning you are unable to understand even the simplest instructions. “Jim, put today’s tablet in your pill box.”

“I don't understand what you mean,” you replied. I tried to be clearer.

“Look Jim, I have opened the flap of the dispenser. Please take the four tablets in this section and transfer them to your pill box.”

“I don't know what you mean.”

“Here Jim, look.” I proceeded to move the four tablets to the pill box, saying, “That's all you had to do.”

“You did not explain it well enough.” You had a good breakfast, then I left for work as it is Adri’s day to stay with you. You fell asleep before I left as usual and Adri had planned to go for a walk with you at 11.00-ish. At 10.40 a.m. Adri started texting me saying you were very confused. You did not understand why he was there and said you didn't want to go for a walk. He also said you were staring into nothingness and were totally unresponsive. I rang home and when I spoke to you, you sounded catatonic and totally disconnected from reality. I really do not know what to do. I will leave work at the beginning of December and may even be placed on garden leave sooner. In theory, I could take over as your full-time carer rather than look for two to three days consultancy work as I had planned. The thought, however, fills me with dread. I do not recognise you. I do not know you any longer. And whilst I feel extreme pity and tenderness for you, I also feel resentment, anger and fear about the future. I am also afraid that this 'you' who I do not like, may wipe out all the memories of the Jim I loved, respected and was in awe of. Life is shit!

Saturday 28th December 2019

It's now almost two months since I checked in. A lot has happened to me during that time. In November, I started going to work only for the three days a week when the carer was in and worked very short days. Then, from 26th November I stopped going to the office completely. I'm still on garden leave, which means that I am at home all the time. I kept Harrie on because my plan is to find some part-time work in the New Year to get me out of the house, earn some money and keep my brain active. Having been at home with you every day has been a benefit and a curse at the same time. We've had many good days together and you seem to have regained some 'normality' and sense of humour. I also try to get out three days a week for a break, while the carer is with you, often to meet with ex-colleagues for lunch. On these occasions I am usually out for less than four hours overall and still arrive home early enough to let Harrie leave a couple of hours before the end of her shift.

However, I have noticed that when I go out to meet friends or colleagues and leave you with Harrie, you play up. You seem to resent the fact that I do not 'want' to be with you all the time now that I am not working. This makes life for Harrie and me harder than expected, but overall it has been okay. You have started going to a couple of INS (Integrated Neurological Services) groups again. You had attended some classes the year before and enjoyed them. Then, one day you felt that one of the instructors placed you in the spotlight and used you as an example in front of the rest of the class. This unwanted attention caused you embarrassment and strain and you walked out of the class, vowing never to return. Because of this incident you were reluctant to go back, but once you did you started to like the groups very much and found that they gave you a lift. At one of these meetings, whilst you were doing your exercises, I started talking to a gentleman who is a carer for his wife. He mentioned the Age UK Centre in Feltham, which also has a number of activities. I need to ensure you join them as well, whenever possible. Christmas this year was spent at home, rather than at our friends, Terrie and Robbie's, as is our custom. Instead, we will go there on 1st January for our traditional Christmas dinner, as that is the day when everyone is available. There will be fifteen of us. On Christmas Day, Adri and Truc cooked and served a delicious meal at home. The kitchen looked like a bomb site, but the meal was excellent and the evening very pleasant. We played games and had a few drinks and you joined in and kept in good spirits. On Boxing Day, the weather was atrocious and we did not go for a walk nor did we do any exercises indoors. We went to bed at approximately midnight and everything seemed okay. You woke up at 3.30 a.m., very confused and needing the toilet. I walked with you and instructed you to sit on the bowl, etc. I was tired so my tone may have been a bit harsh and when I bent down to try to pull your pants up, you hit me and pushed me away. You took your pants off and I said, “Okay, now move out of the way as I need the loo.” You stopped me from going passed you, so I pushed you aside. You stormed back towards the bedroom while I had a wee and when I tried to get back into the bedroom you closed the door on me. I pushed the door open and you fell onto the bed. Then you started calling our son,

“Adri, Adri.” He came to see what was happening and you told him I was trying to kill you. Adri used his usual gentle manner to calm you down and explained that I love you and would not harm you in any way. I petulantly added that you were the one who attacked me, even if it was a very weak punch, and I can push you away whenever I want. It is clear that in your confused state you feel that you are just defending yourself when you behave in this manner. And when I think rationally I understand that, but when we are in the midst of it, I find all of this so unfair and painful to accept and I react very angrily.

I am not ill and I should be able to remain calm and try to get you out of whatever psychosis you are in at the time, but often I am ashamed to admit, my rage and resentment seem to prevail. This only aggravates the situation. After Adri’s calming words, you accepted that I was not trying to kill you and we went back to sleep. I had set the alarm for nine o'clock, so that we could get to the cinema at 11.30 a.m. to see ‘Little Women’.

However, after the events of the night, I decided to switch off the alarm and sleep on. When you woke up at 10.30 a.m. we showered, dressed and had breakfast as usual. At 12.00 p.m., we were ready to go for a walk and decided to remain in Feltham as we had to collect your medicines from Asda. We walked to the chemist without any major upset and collected your medicines. On the way back, you started walking with your head slumped forward, more than usual. The weight of your head pulling you down meant that you ended up running. I asked you to straighten up and push your shoulders back. You tried unsuccessfully. I then grabbed your arm and raised it to keep you straight. By the time we arrived home I was exhausted and I am sure you were too. We went inside the house. I took your jacket off and noticed that you were still very slumped forward. I was seriously concerned, as there are a lot of obstacles in the house and you could have easily lost your balance and fallen on something. I asked you to sit down, but you did not seem to listen. You eventually got close enough to the sofa for me to push you on to it. Well, that must have created panic within you, because you stood up quicker than I have seen you move in a while and ran out of the front door. I followed, asking you to come back in but you would not listen. I then grabbed your jacket and ran after you. I tried to put it on as it was cold, but you continued walking away from the house and all the way you kept shouting the names of our neighbours as you passed their houses, asking for help. Suddenly, you turned around and walked back towards the house, the way we had just come. The whole time you kept calling out, "Peter, help me. Jim, help. Donna, help." We arrived home and I opened the door. I tried to help you onto the step as you were very unbalanced, but you turned aggressively towards me and told me to leave you alone. You then fell on the threshold. Not a real fall, more of a sit down on the floor. It was freezing and you were still without a jacket. I begged you to let me help you up, but you kept telling me to keep away from you. Leanne, our next door neighbour, came out and offered to help, but you said you would not go inside the house with me. Kim, another neighbour, was walking past with her dog and also came to assist. She managed to get you inside the house by promising to stay with you until Adri and Truc returned home. They had gone to the gym but I rang to ask them to come back. When they arrived, Kim left and you calmed down. I explained to Adri what had happened and he said that the trigger for your manic reaction must have been me pushing you on to the sofa. Adri and I then discussed the need to explore other options, as I cannot look after you all the time if you believe I am going to harm you. I know you don't believe what you say when you say it, but that does not make it less painful for me. I also know that nudging or pushing you will trigger an aggressive reaction in you but I do it nonetheless, as this is the least of two evils.

Should I not intervene when I do, you would often fall to the ground.

The next day I rang Social Services and asked for a further assessment due to your exponential deterioration.

Monday 6th January 2020

We spent New Year's Eve indoors watching Jools Holland and it was a peaceful and pleasant evening. On New Year's Day, we all went to Robbie and Terrie's for the delayed Christmas feast and, whilst you were extremely quiet, you were okay. The next few days were also okay. In fact, they were pleasant enough for me to think that I should stop looking for work and become your full-time carer. We went to the cinema, for walks and had a good time together. On Sunday morning we went to Twickenham for a walk, visited a little gallery and in the evening we went to the local Nepalese Restaurant with Adri and Truc. During the meal, Adri remarked that you seemed better these days and we had a pleasant evening. We went to bed at 11.30 p.m. and you woke up at 2.30 a.m. for your toilet call. You went by yourself but I knew you had not done anything because you were in and out too quickly. I asked if you needed help and followed you back into the toilet. You tried to sit down but your lack of spatial ability meant that you would have fallen onto the floor had I not intervened. I manoeuvred you onto the bowl, very gently I thought, but this triggered your paranoia again and you became extremely agitated. You spent the next few hours getting in and out of bed, saying that you are afraid of me. At 6.30 a.m. you agreed to take your tablets, which thankfully worked almost immediately. You fell asleep and slept until 10.00 a.m. When you opened your eyes, however, I could see you were still out of it and appeared scared. I asked if you remembered what had happened during the night and you said you did. You added that I was a liar and a cheat and that you would get dressed and 'get out of here'. You opened the wardrobe and started pulling shirts and trousers onto the floor. You tried to get dressed but obviously weren't able to put anything on by yourself. I asked if I could help but you shouted and swore at me. I left the bedroom and went downstairs. After a few seconds I could hear you say, "Hello, Cathy, Hello." I climbed back upstairs and you apologised. You looked so sad and contrite and I felt real affection and pity for you. You said that you were an idiot and you would not do anything like this again.

We got ready, waited for Harrie to arrive, then drove to the Age UK office in Bedfont to see what activities were available.

Tuesday 14 January 2020

We had a terrible night, after an equally bad evening. I cannot even remember how or why we started arguing. I seem to recall you saying something antagonistic, just because I asked you a question. I know that I totally flipped and I scared myself. I seemed possessed and kept saying, "You are driving me to a mental home!" You then reacted with equal rage and kicked your little table with all the paraphernalia on it. Everything fell on the floor and water spilled on the carpet. You then looked really afraid and kept saying,

"Please Cath, please let us be okay." I, in turn, came to my senses and gave you a kiss and a big hug. We then had dinner together. However, the residue of the confrontation must have followed you into the night and you had a very restless sleep. Between 3.00 a.m. and 7.00 a.m. you must have sat up on the bed then laid down again twenty times. Every single time I had to raise your legs onto the bed and cover you up. At 10.30 a.m. I drove you and Harrie to the Age UK Day Centre, or Vintage Club as they call it. I hope you'll enjoy it but I have my doubts. I hung around while I was waiting for Breda, the Centre Coordinator so that I could give her the paperwork and money. Watching you, you looked really lost. Some of the other people introduced themselves to you but when you said your name, they could not hear you as your voice is so soft. I felt so much tenderness and love, and it was heart-wrenching seeing you now so quiet, so out of it all, when you always used to be at the centre of debate and conversation. A week ago Mari, my sister, sent me a text saying that she was listening to 'Every Breath You Take' by the Police and she was reminded of when you used to write down songs for her. That was one of the songs you wrote down and explained to her. Oh my love, you had such a positive impact on so many people.

Wednesday 12 February 2020

A lot has happened over the past month and a half. The saddest news is that my dad died on 5th February. He had been unwell for the past two weeks and I went home to Italy to see him while he was still compos mentis. We were all there, the whole family and it was a warm and loving goodbye. Three days later he died. By then, however, I was already back in London. The funeral was held on 7th February so Adri and I had very little time to make arrangements to attend. We left London on the 6th and returned the next day, straight after the funeral. They were two gruelling days. That was the first time you were left for a night on your own without either Adri or me.

You seemed nervous when we set off for the airport, even though I had arranged for Truc and Harrie to be there at all times with you. We had been gone from home barely one hour when you rang in a frenzy. Adri explained that we were going to my dad's funeral and we would be back the next day. "You are going to a funeral and I am on death row here," you stated. Adri and I could not help smiling at this latest madness. I had prepared a slice of quiche and a bean salad for you but Truc texted to say that you refused to eat it, as you said it was poisoned. You then chose a pie in the fridge and seemed much happier with that. All this was communicated to us via text, of course. On our return, we learnt that you had slept very little. There is no denying that your mind is fast deteriorating and it is almost impossible to have a normal conversation with you, beyond basic pleasantries. You have also started to become paranoid more regularly and for no apparent reason.

Today I was going out with Terrie and Cathy for lunch while Adri was at home with you, as he was working from home. You seemed okay when you got up. You had a good night's sleep and a hearty breakfast. You then asked what was happening today. Adri replied that you would go for a walk with him, get the newspaper and go to Costa for a coffee. You asked, "Who is employing me?"

"Jim, what are you talking about? Nobody is employing you. You are my husband, Adri's dad, and you and I are both retired." I replied.

"I know I am homeless and you can throw me out anytime you want."

"Jim, you are not homeless."

"This is your home," Adri interjected. "Dad, put your jacket on and let's go for a walk." Off they went and ten minutes later I left to meet my friends. I texted Adri to see how you were and he said that you rambled on for a bit but then calmed down.

It is becoming so difficult and tiring taking care of you. Even last night, before going to bed, you were restless and angry after a difficult visit to the toilet. You kept asking me to talk to you while wandering up and down the room. I had almost no voice due to a cold and a sore throat. I kept saying that everything is okay and that I found it painful to talk. All I wanted was to watch a TV programme but you would not leave me alone. You kept walking in front of me, begging me to talk to you. I hated you at that moment, because I never seem to have any time to myself.

Thursday 13th February 2020

3.00 p.m.: We just had another terrible argument. You are now sleeping in your chair, leaving me trying to work out what has happened. What started this terrible confrontation? We got up at 9.15 a.m. after a decent night. We showered, dressed and went downstairs to have breakfast. Adri was working from home, as he had a meeting at 2.00 p.m. in Chiswick and felt it would be easier to travel directly from home. After breakfast I told you that there was more than one hour before I drove you to your Tai Chi class at 11.45 a.m. so I turned the radio on. Adri carried on with whatever he was doing; either talking on the phone or working on his laptop. He had said hello to us when we first arrived downstairs and had asked how we had slept and told us he had a lot on. You looked at me in a secretive way and asked why Adri was not talking to us. I replied that he was busy working and had no time to talk to us at the moment. You asked, "How is it going to work with us running two businesses?" I told you that only Adri has a business as we are both retired. I said that I had been trying to find part-time work but it seemed unlikely that I would find a job at a senior level, that is part-time and does not require travel. These restrictions are obviously due to the fact that you require twenty-four hour care. You didn't seem convinced but we set off for Tai Chi, where you had a good session. On the way back, we stopped at Tesco to buy some food. And when we reached the car I asked you to hold the trolley whilst I transferred the shopping into bags. I am not sure what you understood but you started shouting at me. I asked you what was wrong and you said that I treat you like an idiot. I kept quiet, got into the car and drove home. When we arrived home, Adri was on his way out to his meeting. He carried the bags in for us and then left, saying, "See you later. I may come straight home after the meeting. So, not too late." We both entered the house and you started ranting.

"Nobody speaks to me in this house. I am the lowest of the low and nobody pays attention to me." I totally lost it. I pointed out that I have no life of my own, as most of my time is spent taking care of you, driving you to classes and keeping you occupied. You came towards me with your hands out towards my neck as if you wanted to choke me. I pushed you away, screaming,

"I could kick you to the ground anytime I want, you are so weak. Do not come at me like this again - I will push you hard next time."

"I will kill you; call the law," you screamed.

"You are so pathetic. Why can't you be a decent human being? Why do you have to be nasty and aggressive with the people who care and look after you?" I cried.

"I am sorry, let's start again," you said fearfully.

"I am fed up hearing you say you are sorry and half an hour later behaving in the same way," I said.

"Whatever I say now it is not going to be good enough, is it Cath?"

"Yes, what you say is useless. What you do is what counts. For once, after you say sorry, stop this appalling behaviour." You laboriously proceeded to put on your jacket and said,

"I need some money to stay somewhere."

"You idiot. This is your house, you live here. You cannot stay anywhere else because you cannot look after yourself. You cannot dress or undress yourself. You cannot wipe your arse. You cannot feed yourself. Where do you think you can go? The only place you can go is a care home. Is that what you want? Do you want me to look for one? Otherwise, you will have to stay here, in the hope that you change your behaviour."

"Is that office still open to me?"

"What office? What are you talking about, Jim? If you mean our home, then yes, you can stay here. It is our home, mine and yours." You then fell asleep. I feel terrible for the bullying I subjected you to again, but I cannot stand my life as it is at present. Any time we have an argument now you ask for money to get away. You have a debit card but cash seems to be the only currency you trust. You have never been interested in money. As long as we had enough for the bare necessities, you were happy. You are not a materialistic person and you never spent money on yourself. When we first met, you used to buy all your clothes from charity shops, out of need most of the time, but also because you did not care what you were wearing. I had returned from Italy in June 1980, just a few days after I had left, to help out in my family restaurant for the summer, because you were having a meltdown without me there. So we looked for a place to live together. We found the bedsit in Maida Vale and you went back to your place to collect your stuff. You returned with a medium-sized suitcase and I asked whether you were collecting the rest later. "This is all I have," you said. You did not need money for books as, in those days, you borrowed them from libraries. Even then, despite not being able to afford to buy books, you always bought The Guardian each day. Alcohol and cigarettes were your expensive habit, but you gave up smoking over twenty years ago. You can now drink very little alcohol as it affects you badly. You still enjoy a glass of wine with Adri in the evening, when we go out for a meal or to the cinema. You also enjoy a Scotch with me but that is it. You introduced me to Single Malt Scotch and we now have a little drink at night together. You put some water in your whisky and I used to take ice in mine. Recently, however, you have begun to struggle to get the ice cubes out of the tray, so I take it neat as you like getting the whisky for me. It is one of the few things you can still do for me.

The only piece of jewellery you ever wore is your wedding ring and you would not wear or want any other jewellery. Clothes also did not interest you. You could wear the same things over and over again and I had to buy new items for you to wear or you would not have bothered. As long as we were together and Adri was okay, you were happy.

You were always very concerned about Adri's financial circumstances and you kept saying that you wanted to give him one of your pension pots. I had to tell you that would not be a good idea. You knew how much I would have liked a house in Richmond with a view of the river, because water reminded me of my native home, Tremosine on Lake Garda. That was pie in the sky, obviously, but it was nice to dream. You often said, "When I win the lottery, I will buy that home with the river view that you want so much." You wanted to please me so badly but obviously not badly enough as you never played the lottery. Now, with everything slipping away from you, you feel that you need cash in case you need to get yourself a place to stay and you have started obsessing about your wallet. You hide it, forget where you have put it and search for it, then check how much cash you have in it. It contains only twenty-five pounds in cash. That would not get you very far. Somehow you feel that your debit card is not good enough.

Saturday 22nd February 2020

You are watching the Italy versus Scotland rugby match. I'm grabbing this time to update this diary. Last Thursday you had a doctor's appointment. The surgery had called, saying they needed to review your care plan and I assumed they needed to check your medications. When we saw the doctor, however, it was clear that the care review was not what I had expected. The doctor advised us that she wanted to carry out a memory test. She started by asking you the current month and year and you correctly said February 2020. She then asked you to count back from twenty. Again, you did it correctly. She continued by giving you a name and address that you needed to remember a bit later. 'John Smith, 42 High Street, Bedfont'. Just a few minutes later you were able to recall 'Mr Smith', 'High Street' and 'Bedfont', but you could not remember the first name of the person or the road number. The doctor then mentioned three words and asked you to memorise them: 'banana, chair and sunrise'. She asked you to recite the months backwards from December, but you were totally unable to even start this exercise. When she asked you to repeat the three words, you could only recall 'banana'. The doctor then asked what you enjoy doing. As you did not answer, I said, "What did you enjoy doing, Jim, in the past?" Again, I witnessed that lost expression on your face and no answer. I tried to prompt you by saying, "You used to love reading, films, music, crosswords and puzzles of any kind. In short, the arts and intellectual stimulations." Hearing that, you seemed to come back to life and added that you still like going for a walk and the cinema is still quite enjoyable. Walking is indeed something you still like doing. Up until a few months ago you used to do your ten thousand steps each day, then every night you would show me your pedometer with pride. Recently, on good days you still manage up to six thousand steps a day. Your daily walk takes you to Costa Coffee in Feltham and back home. At the weekend, if the weather is nice, you and I go further afield. We like walking on the riverbank in Twickenham and at times, Kingston and Staines. When we feel very adventurous we may go for a walk in Bushy Park or Kew Gardens. The doctor asked if you had difficulty concentrating when, for example, you watch TV. You did not reply, so I told her that you have a very short concentration span and cannot follow any programme for longer than a few minutes. I also added that you have lost interest in almost everything. The doctor then advised that she would put together a care plan for you, in case you lose the ability to make decisions. She added that you could give me power of attorney, so that I could make decisions on your behalf, should the need arise. I responded that you may struggle with losing your independence. But the doctor seems to believe, from your reaction, that you are okay with this. She proceeded to give us some literature to read and discuss. We will need to see her again the week after next to finalise details. The match has finished and you move towards the downstairs toilet. We had it installed because you were struggling to get up and down the stairs. With help from Adri and me you can still make it upstairs at night then back down in the morning but tackling the stairs three or four times each day has become an unsurmountable task for you. You open the door and ask if anyone is in there. "Jim, it is just you and me in the house." You go inside the toilet and lower your trousers but, as usual, you are unable to position yourself right in front of the bowl in order to sit on it. I say, "Jim, side-step towards the sink."

"Leave me alone." As I leave the toilet you follow, saying that you did not understand what I said. We both return and I nudge you into position. You sit down and ask me what you need to do next.

"Have a piss, a pee, a wee. That is why we came in here in the first place." You proceed to pee, then ask me what you need to do next. I point at the toilet roll and ask, "What do you need this for?"

"To wipe my penis." You stand up, wipe your penis and then throw the paper into the toilet. "Do I need to wash my hands?"

"Yes, you do." You sit in your armchair and start crying. You say you do not know how to face life and add that you will die alone. I feel such sadness; it is tragic to witness your pain.

"No, you will not," I tell you. "Adri and I are not going to leave you, no matter what." You calm down and start watching the Wales versus France rugby match. When we left the doctor's surgery on Thursday it was raining quite heavily, but I pulled your hood up and opened the umbrella for us both. After walking twenty metres from the surgery, you accused me of lying and cheating. I replied that I told the doctor the truth. You then said that you would rather be anywhere than with me and proceeded to turn away from me and walk in the opposite direction. As it was raining, I said that you needed to get home, then you could choose not to talk to me if you did not want to. We somehow managed to make it home. All the way, you were ranting and raving, saying that you do not have a pot to piss in and that I am a shit. How can you not recognise what we have and what I am doing for you now that you are so incapacitated? It is so hard not to resent these words spilling from your mouth. Adri was working from home and I mouthed to him that you were having a mad episode. He managed to calm you down and the evening proceeded without any further incidents. We went to sleep at 11.00 p.m., as normal, and you fell asleep immediately. You woke up at approximately 3.00 a.m. and were in and out of bed for the next three hours. I suggested you should take your tablets so that you could sleep a few extra hours but you kept saying, "No." I am sure you felt that I was trying to poison you, as you often accuse me of doing.

Eventually, you took the tablets and slept until 8.30 a.m. After getting ready, we went downstairs and I started making porridge, whilst you attempted to get your boots on. You asked me to help you and I asked you to try again. "You have all day, Jim. Try again and if you cannot do it, I will help you." You threw the boot at me and came towards me with your eyes popping out and your hands positioned to strangle me once again. Your favourite way of attacking me, it seems. You suddenly stopped and dropped your hands by your side as you realised how wrong it was and you backed off. As I have mentioned a few times, I can easily push you away from me as you are very weak. You never actually hurt me but this does not detract from the fact that I feel upset, humiliated and hurt every time you display this violent streak towards me.

On this occasion, even though you stopped mid-flow, I grabbed your jumper, put my face right up to yours and said, "Stop doing this you mad dog, or I will start attacking you as well." We must have been shouting because Leanne, our neighbour, knocked on the door looking concerned and said, "Jim, wouldn't you be better off in a Care Home?" At that moment I agreed with her, as I feel I cannot cope with you any longer. You calmed down and apologised but I told you that I cannot look after you if you attack me all the time and you do not trust me. I rang Puneet from Social Services and asked her for information on assisted accommodation.

Adri called later that night to check how we were and I told him that I was seriously considering assisted accommodation. On the Friday, I took you to music therapy. Adri worked from home and the day passed without drama. We went to bed quite late, at approximately midnight, but you were unable to fall asleep until 1.00 a.m. You then slept very well until 9.30 this morning, waking only for two trips to the toilet. Whilst dressing you, I asked you to let go of the grab rail and hold on to me to stop you from shaking. "Are you calling me stupid?" you said, putting your hands around my neck. I saw red and pushed you onto the bed. You started screaming, "Stop, stop." Adri rushed into the bedroom and I told him what had happened. He repeated that you need to stop attacking me or I will not be able to look after you and you will not be able to stay at home. You looked desperate, "I have no warning when it happens. I have tried to stop but this happens again and again." All this you said through tears and extreme pain. I looked at you and I also felt like crying.

"Adri, maybe I should not react when Dad becomes aggressive but I feel so hurt and angry every time, then I counter-attack, which is really counterproductive."

"Mum, you should try not to react because it will happen again. He cannot help it. Parkinson's has taken everything from him."

"I love him very much and putting him in a care home would be evil," I said.

"It would be so tragic for Dad. If you could get two or three day's respite, you may be able to cope," Adri suggested. I keep changing my mind, because I love you so much, even though you are no longer the man I married. You have become someone who, at times, I do not like at all.

"Mum, you should write about the good times with Dad, or you will forget and all you will have is this. I should do it as well, because I almost do not remember what he used to be like."

"I have started to do that Adri but it is mostly about the last tragic year, unfortunately." I replied.

"What are you doing today? Do you need me around for anything?" Adri asked.

"No thanks, we are going for a coffee and a walk."

You and I are at Costa Coffee in Twickenham with the newspaper. I open it for you at the concise crossword page. I get the drinks and when I return you say, "The crossword is the same as yesterday."

"What do you mean, do you recall all the clues?"

"Look - one, two, three."

"Jim, that is the grid with the numbers. The clues are next to the grid. Can you see?" My clever, beautiful love, reduced to such limited brain activity. Oh, the sadness and anger I feel for what you have become. And, of course, the sheer terror of what the future holds for us. Where have you gone, Amore? Where is the man who used to do the Guardian cryptic crossword? The man who used to love his Guardian and read it religiously every day. Always looking for articles on Italy and highlighting them to me and, at times, even reading them to me. The person who could not go to sleep without reading a few pages of the book he had on the go. You'd say, "I have read the same lines for the past five minutes. Shall we go to sleep?"

"Okay, my love."

"Good night."

"Good night, Amore." We kissed and I would turn on my side, facing away from you. You would 'spoon' me, adding almost every night,

"This is the best part of the day." We would fall asleep with music on.

At weekends, you would get up, shower and then bring me toast and coffee in bed and often we made love before I got up. The days were so full of expectation with you. You could always entertain me, make me laugh and excite me. You used to tell me silly jokes, especially about the Irish, as you'd say that being Irish you could do that.

One of our favourite jokes was the one about the Irish man looking at a man with his hand immersed in a fish tank and the little fish swimming in and out through the man's fingers, slalom like. 'That is great,' said the Irish man. 'How do you do that?'

'It is the power of the mind,' replied the man, removing his hand from the tank and leaving the room. Upon his return to the room, the man saw the Irish man with his hand in the tank and his mouth closing and opening fish-like. It is a funny, but cruel joke and at times I fear that you may be turning into that Irishman, my love.

Wednesday 26th February 2020

10.30 a.m.: We've had a very bad night and morning. Puneet will be coming here tomorrow for another assessment. We went to bed last night before 11.00 p.m. because you were very restless and could not concentrate on anything. I was trying to watch a drama on TV but you kept getting up, sitting down and asking me to talk to you. Once in bed, you fell asleep almost immediately but it was a very disturbed sleep. You woke up at 1.30 a.m. and, as usual, you sat up on the bed, fiddling with the bed clothes and uncovering me. I asked if you needed the toilet and you said no but ten minutes later you were up again. This continued for the next two hours. At 3.30 a.m. I became angry as I was very tired and I asked you to lie down and have a rest. You would not respond, so I tried to lower your head onto the pillow by applying light pressure on your forehead. You clearly did not like this and started kicking and punching me with both hands. I cupped your face with my hands to stop you but you tried to head butt me. I was very upset and left our bedroom to go to the spare room, next door. I could hear you dragging things out of the wardrobe and after twenty minutes came back to our room to find clothes strewn on the floor and you holding socks in your hands. When I asked what you were doing, you said you were trying to get some clothes together to run away. I felt so sad for you and for me. I asked if you wanted me to come back to bed with you and you said yes. Unfortunately you were still very agitated and another half hour of flailing and thrashing ensued. You must have been in hell and I felt such compassion and love for you. I said, "Take your tablets and you may fall asleep for a few hours. I will also do your hair to relax you." You lay down and I started to stroke your hair. After twenty minutes you were asleep. It had just turned 5.30 a.m. At 7.30 a.m. Truc left for work. Hearing the front door open, you woke up again. You started coughing and seemed to be chesty. I asked you to try to rest for a bit longer as you'd had a very bad night but you were unable to relax and kept sitting up on the bed with those eyes of yours; totally manic. At 8.00 a.m. we got up. I rang the doctor and managed to get an emergency appointment for 11.40 a.m., as I was sure that your behaviour indicated another infection. I had prepared porridge and asked you to stand by the dining room table so that I could help you sit down. I aligned the chair behind you and touched the back of your knees, so that you could feel the chair and sit on it. However, this action that I do every morning, on this occasion triggered another violent reaction from you. I was tired and upset and lost my temper completely and, with it, any shred of pity and compassion. I am ashamed to admit that I proceeded to bully you. There is no other way to describe what I did to you. I mocked the way you walk and called you all the names under the sun, "Moronic idiot, violent, aggressive pig, shithead. You do not understand anything, you moron." This painful, cruel and disgusting verbal attack, that I am now so embarrassed about, stopped only when we went to the doctor who confirmed that you have a chest infection.

1.25 p.m.: We are back home now but things are no better. I had to push you into the car and drag you out of it because you could not make it on your own. This triggered your rage again and when I tried to help you sit down by holding your hand and directing your legs, you punched me. I am disgusted about the verbal abuse I subjected you to but your behaviour awakes some sort of deep-seated primordial instinct and I become like a woman possessed. Your aggression, your needs, your incompetence and your total lack of recognition for what I do, turn me into a person I dislike intensely. I used to feel outrage when people expressed disdain for the way Social Services treated their relatives. "Why don't you look after them yourself, instead of delegating responsibilities to Social

Services?" I used to say. Now I fully understand why you would want a loved one to be taken care of by someone who does it as a job. On the other hand, even if at times I think about it, I know I could not put you into a care home, because it would be terrible for you and for our love. Moreover, you are the perfect subject for abuse, because you can be aggressive, mouthy and you don't listen. And that's why I feel I could never do it to you. I am really concerned about your mental state. You are sitting on the sofa, picking up items from the table, moving them about and mumbling all the time. I came near you to give you a cuddle and gently said, "Stop it, stop it, please." But you pushed me away, saying,

"Do you think I am stupid?" You stood at the door, looking out onto the road. I was not sure what you were planning to do, given you can hardly stand up. Now you are outside and the automatic door shut behind you. You are trying to get back in and look puzzled by the door. I open it for you from the inside and you come back in. You say you need a piss but you do not want my help and you are unable to do it by yourself. This is sheer hell.

Friday 28 February 2020

Just when I think that things cannot get any worse, they unfortunately do. On Wednesday evening, before going to bed you didn't want to go to the toilet and you said again that you were afraid of me. Therefore, after I lifted your legs onto the bed and covered you up, I said I was going to let you stay in our room on your own. I went next door to sleep in the spare room. At 3.30 a.m. I heard you moving about. I came to see how you were and you said, "I am in the rain." This, I soon translate into

"I wet the bed." I took the wet bedding off and helped you onto my side of the bed, which was dry. I went back to the spare room. After half an hour I heard a loud bang. I rushed into the room and found you on the floor, having fallen out of bed. My side of the bed has no railing and you must have turned and fallen, banging your head on the bedside. I cleaned and disinfected the head wound and then we got into bed together as you did not want to be on your own. You appeared scared, but thankfully not of me. I put three towels over the wet part of the bed and somehow we managed to sleep until 8.00 a.m. Due to the bad night we'd just had, we decided that you could not go to Tai Chi. We walked to Tesco to get the newspaper, but you were very tired and shaky and as soon as we were back home you fell asleep. When you awoke, you said you needed the toilet but you would not let me touch you. I quickly pulled your trousers down and nudged you on to the bowl. This enraged you but you had a wee. You stood up and somehow managed to pull your trousers up but could not close them and would not let me do it. We turned the TV on. You tried to sit in your armchair, without success. You then wandered up and down the length of the house for twenty minutes, then asked me to take your jumper off as you were too hot. In the house it was indeed nice and warm, but outside was very cold – two or three degrees at most. It was obvious that you were still unable to sit down and I offered to help. You let me take your hands but when I tried to walk you towards the sofa so that you could sit, you struggled and cursed. As you were close enough to the sofa I nudged you onto it, aware of the potential consequences. "You are trying to kill me! Stay away from me!" you shouted. Because of the rage and the adrenalin, you were able to stand up quickly and went straight outside.

"Jim, it is freezing, you have only a vest on and you have a chest infection. Please come back in and let me put your jumper on," I pleaded.

"No, I don't trust you. Leanne, help!" you shouted. I then knocked on Leanne's door and asked her to help me get you back inside. With her help, you came back into the house. You sat down and fell asleep. When you woke up, you immediately said you wanted to go for a walk.

"Let me put your jumper and jacket on, then," I said. You allowed me to do that but when I tried to put your hat on, you started screaming again. When you left the house it was getting dark, so I decided to follow you at a distance. I asked Leanne to watch out in case you returned without me and I gave her the code to open the door and let you in, if required. I parked the car at Tesco and waited for you to arrive, then I followed you a few steps behind, on foot. When you reached the square in Feltham, you started rummaging through your pockets. You undid your jacket and kept searching. I then approached you, asked what you were looking for and offered to do your jacket up again as it was extremely cold. You told me to get lost and walked back towards the High Street. You crossed the road but could not step onto the kerb on the other side and fell in the road where there was a bus approaching. I put a hand up and the bus stopped immediately. I pulled you off the road onto the pavement with great difficulty. You were screaming. Two passers-by helped me stand you up. You were very shaken and you held on to me like a child. We walked to the car in silence and you let me help you get in. We drove home. We went to bed at 10.45 p.m. and you fell asleep very quickly. At 2.30 a.m. you woke up and the same painful routine occurred - you going to the toilet, not knowing what to do. Me trying to help you and talking you through the steps. After half an hour of pleading and coaxing you were quite near the bowl. I nudged you onto it and pulled your pants down. You started screaming. Adri was not at home but Truc heard the commotion and came to see what was going on. For the next two and a half hours you proceeded to scream, “Call the police, 195 Rochester Avenue.” Then you started singing in a loud voice and began drumming your fingers on the door quite loudly. Truc and I begged you to stop as you would wake up our neighbours. You would not listen, so Truc and I decided to go downstairs in the hope that you would calm down. Eventually, at 5.30 a.m. you went for a wee – you must have been bursting - took your Sinemet tablets and fell asleep. You slept until 9.00 a.m. but due to the terrible night, we decided not to go to music therapy. Instead, at 11.30 a.m. we went to Staines to pick up the newspaper and a coffee. Unfortunately, you were so tired that you almost dropped off at Cafe Nero. You had a full cup of coffee in your hands, which spilled all over your clothes. We returned home and I made you a sandwich but you could not hold it in your hands and threw it back on the plate, saying that you were going for a walk. I begged you not to go out, as it was raining quite heavily. You did not listen and left home at 3.00 p.m. You did not want to pull your hood up either.

It is now 4.30 p.m. and you are not back yet. I am so worried about your wellbeing, so guilty for not being able to keep my cool when you are irrational and so angry with you, Parkinson’s and the Social Services for not giving me the help I feel I require to keep us both safe.

Saturday 29th February 2020

After a reasonably good night we visited Staines again. We had some refreshments and I suggested that we went for a walk. We started walking towards the river but you said you were exhausted and I was dragging you for a walk. I reluctantly agreed to drive back home. As soon as we walked through the door you asked me if I would go with you for a pint. I explained that you cannot have alcohol as you are on antibiotics and added that you had complained of being exhausted just twenty minutes earlier. You replied that you would then go by yourself and started to walk out of the door without your jacket again. It was another bitterly cold day, so I pulled you back and said you could not go out without a jacket. You marched to the back door and out into the garden, still without a jacket. I tried to get you in and attempted to put your jacket on. You kept saying, “Call the police.” You then started calling out for Leanne. She came out into her garden and asked you to go back inside. You would not relent and kept making negative comments about me. We agreed with Leanne that she should come round to see if she could convince you to either come back in or put your jacket on. I let Leanne into the house and through into our garden but you refused to listen to her, so she returned home. I was very concerned because of the low temperature, your chest infection and light clothes. I rang Adri, who was in South Africa on business and put him on speaker, in the hope that he could try to convince you to go back in, but even our son did not succeed. I then decided to call 999 because I did not know what else to do. When the paramedics arrived, approximately forty-five minutes later, they managed to get you back into the house. They wrapped you in a blanket to warm you up and then they took your temperature, blood pressure and checked your other vital signs. They said that everything seemed okay. You had calmed down a lot by then, so they decided that taking you to the hospital would not be helpful, given the adverse effect the hospital had on you in the past. I agreed. It is now 6.30 p.m. The paramedics have left and you are asleep. I am truly dis-tressed, upset and at a total loss regarding what to do. My every waking moment is dedicated to you. If you want to go to bed I follow you, as I need to undress you and tuck you in. And if I do not get in with you, you usually call me. The same goes for the mornings - you decide when to get up.

Tuesday 3rd March 2020

Adri came back from South Africa this morning. He was telling us about Johannesburg and how it is a broken society, divided by haves and have-nots rather than totally by black and white, even though this goes hand in hand most of the time. You showed no interest at all. Halfway through the conversation, you asked if you could visit Bristol Court before moving in. I said that yes, of course we would, but this is not going to happen immediately, if at all. Puneet, the adult social worker came back yesterday, after I reached out to her saying that I am at breaking point and needed help. I did mention the possibility of assisted accommodation to her as you often say, when we argue, that you would like a place of your own. Puneet wanted to ascertain if that was indeed what you wanted. She mentioned Bristol Court as an option, providing you meet the criteria. We need to find out costs as well. She said that these things take time. I told her that we would consider day centres for respite care, such as HomeLink, which would be a less drastic solution. I informed her that we applied three months ago, for a two or three day respite but I had received no response. This would give me a break and, I think, would be a much better solution than living apart. Before she left, you told Puneet that is also the solution you would prefer. You are now asleep in your chair and your chest infection has not gone yet. You could not go to Age UK for your vintage club today. I feel so terribly sad about everything. You still look like my clever, beautiful, funny husband, but I do not recognise you in anything you do or say. You have become a frightened, needy, unfriendly person who understands very little of what goes on around you. You have no grasp of reality. And your world must be a really scary place. For some reason, the more frightened you are, the more aggressive you become towards me. The days must be so long for you now. You have even stopped watching TV. You keep it on but it is clear that you are not listening, watching or taking anything in. You've stopped all activities that gave you pleasure: reading, crosswords, politics, jokes, cinema and music. However, music still helps to awake some sort of response in you as does Adri and, at times, me. But that is all. You have also regressed even further in your spatial awareness. The day before yesterday you tried to sit down in your chair but you totally missed it and fell onto the floor. Thankfully, just on to your bottom. Truc and I helped you back on to your chair but you were naturally shaken. I cannot begin to imagine how worried and scared of the future you must be and this fills my heart with anguish.

How can I be so callous and react badly to you, rather than be kind all the time, even when you are nasty and mean to me? I am not sick and should be able to modify my response, instead of reacting angrily and with sarcasm. I feel such a shit thinking about my plight, when you must be in hell.

5.00 p.m.: This is a summary of the past half hour: You called out, "I need to stand up, help me."

"Jim, you need to try to do it by yourself as the physio told you to," I replied.

"Do you think I am doing this for fun? I cannot do it."

"Jim, please put your hands on the side of the chair, use your legs, lean forward and say one, two, three, up." With this, you managed to get up by yourself. You walked to the kitchen. You put tonic water in a glass and came back into the living room. You looked confused. I asked you to put the glass down on your little table. You did that and then went back to the kitchen, coming back with an empty glass. I told you that you did not need an empty glass as your little table was already crowded. You looked at me, puzzled. I gently took the glass from your hands and put it back in the kitchen. When I returned, you asked if you could sit down on the sofa next to me. I said, "Of course you can, my love." You sat down and I noticed that your chin was soaking wet with dribble. I picked up a tissue to wipe it and you pounced on me like a wild animal and tried to hit me. The shock and surprise brought tears to my eyes. Adri, who was working in the room at the time, witnessed the whole scene. He came towards you.

"Dad, you must stop attacking Mum or you will not be able to live here any longer. Mum was just trying to help you."

"I am sorry. I am very sorry," you pleaded.

"Dad, don't say sorry, just don't do it again. Mum cannot look after you if you keep doing this. Would you live with someone who attacks you?"

"I am sorry. I cannot believe it. As soon as I have done it, I know it is wrong. I cannot believe I have done it."

"Dad, I know you are sick. This is not you," Adri said. Turning to me you said,

"Cath, please do not send me to prison. They will kill me in there."

"Jim, we have no intention of sending you to prison but you need to try to stop attacking me," I responded. You look so lost, confused and frightened again. I feel so much love and pity for you.

Wednesday 4th March 2020

3.30 p.m.: Yet again, you have just gone out in the rain without a hat, scarf or umbrella. And still with a chest infection. Thankfully, I ran out after you and managed to put your jacket on, even though you would not allow me to do the buttons up. This morning we went to the surgery again to get additional antibiotics, as your chest infection is not much better. The receptionist said we actually needed to see the doctor to get more antibiotics and gave us an appointment for 4.20 this afternoon. After lunch you went to the toilet and I asked you to wash your hands thoroughly because of Coronavirus. You must have misunderstood what I said, because you started pacing, saying you have no place to go to. I told you that this is your home and you can stay here. You could not relax and said you wanted to go for a walk. I told you we had a doctor's appointment and we could have a walk together after that if you wanted. You walked to the front door and I calmly took your hand and repeated the plan. You seemed to calm down. Twenty minutes later you stood up from your chair and said you were going to let Dice out. When I turned around I noticed you had followed Dice out into the rain without a coat. I did not follow you.

5.00 p.m.: I have just come back from seeing the doctor, with a new set of antibiotics for you. Before I left, I asked Donna, our next door neighbour, to watch out for you in case you returned while I was still out. While I was at the doctor’s surgery my phone rang. “Is this Katie?” (That is the name that appears on the telephone book and is the name everyone has always called me, apart from Jim, who calls me Cathy.)

“Yes, this is Katie.”

“I have James Herdman here at Feltham library and he seems confused,” said the voice on the other end.

“Thanks, I will be there in a minute,” I said. “I am just upstairs at the doctor's.” It is all so tragic.

After your lunch today I asked if you wanted a two bar KitKat but you said no, as you didn't want to put on weight. This is really crazy. You have lost over fifteen kilos in the past eighteen months. There used to be approximately twenty kilos difference in weight between us - you were always between eighteen and twenty-two kilos heavier than I was. Now I am one or two kilos heavier than you are. You have lost so much weight and I’ve put quite a bit on. You certainly would not be able to dance me around the room holding me on your feet. This was one of my favourite peculiarities of yours. I love to dance but you are too self-conscious to do it, even in private. Sometimes, when a particular song came on the radio, I would ask you to dance. When you agreed we would have a slow, sensual jig around the house, until you became embarrassed and started playing the fool. More often, however, you would ask me to get on your feet and then you would dance around very slowly, carrying me with you. There are so many quirky things that I loved about you. When you were dressing yourself, you would sit on the bed to put your socks on, whilst I, still lying in bed, watched you. Without fail, you would pick up one sock to put on your foot and you would lie the other one very gently over my eyes. When we went to the pub you were always trying to catch the beer mats you flicked up, in mid-air. When you smoked, you used to throw your cigarette up in the air and try to catch it in your mouth. So many memories.

Thursday 5th March 2020

We are at Age UK for your Tai Chi Class. You are by far the most disabled person there but you enjoy the class and like the trainer and the music. Music again; so many memories. You used to sing me snippets from your favourite musicals and ask me to guess which one it was. "South Pacific?"

"No."

"The King and I?"

"No."

"Oklahoma?"

"Yes, well done." I could never get the right musical but it was a way to entertain ourselves and flirt. Another regular test you gave me was to guess the crooner who was singing on the radio. You loved your crooners, especially Frank Sinatra, who I now manage to recognise all the time. For the rest, it is hit and miss. A crooner comes on the radio: "Who is singing?"

"Jim Reeves?"

"No."

"Nat King Cole?"

"No. He has Italian heritage."

"Perry Como?"

"Well done, my love." You could never understand how I could continually not guess Dean Martin. You felt that he was so recognisable with his 'lazy' voice. You also loved your classical music, especially piano music. You would often say, "I do not recognise any pieces but I really love listening to it. I would love to be able to play a musical instrument, but I am not musical unfortunately. However, my real dream job would be as a conductor of an orchestra." Very often you pretended to direct, by making exaggerated movements with your arms and abandoning your head with languor. We both love Billie Holliday, Amy Winehouse, Leonard Cohen, Neil Young and Van Morrison. For Christmas, our present to each other was two tickets to the London Palladium to see Van Morrison live on 26th March. I cannot wait and I am sure we shall both enjoy it. During your time in Italy, you came to appreciate Lucio Dalla. I asked you a month ago which song you associate with us, with our love. Without hesitation you said, "Neil Young's 'Comes a Time', the whole CD." When we first got together, that was indeed the music we played every night for almost a year whilst falling asleep. It was a tape played on a portable tape recorder, which has always been associated with the flourishing of our love. On this very CD there is also the first song for which I asked you to write down the words for me all those years ago: 'Four strong winds'. The first of many you wrote down for me. We have always been so in love and we could not bear it when we were apart. It seems as though all that love, in your confused state, has turned to hate. Oh, how I wish we could go back in time to feel that love again. I remember when we went to Wembley Arena to see Leonard Cohen and you were so tender and loving. Looking at me bemused whilst I sang along with Leonard. You bought me a Leonard Cohen hat and a t-shirt with 'I am your man' printed on the front. At the INS centre you attend music therapy classes and, whilst you were sceptic at first, you learnt to enjoy it. There are musical instruments for you to practise on, but the main purpose of the class is to relax the participants through music. When you finished your first class, one of the centre's volunteers asked you how you got on and you said, "Very well, I came third."

"That is excellent," replied the volunteer, enthusiastically.

"Yes, there were only three of us," you replied with a grin on your face. That wicked, dry humour of yours again. I am watching you exercise but you do not move very much at all. Despite trying, somehow you cannot keep up with the moves. You are holding on to your chair, doing nothing. You are now rubbing the back of your waist as the teacher instructed a few minutes ago. Everyone else has now moved on to rubbing their tummy but you continue with the rubbing of your waist. They have changed moves again but you stand still. Before the end of the lesson, I had to come over to ask you if you wanted to leave, as you were just standing in the same spot like a statue, not even looking in the direction of the trainer.

Monday 9th March 2020

10.30 a.m.: You are so restless. And so tired. I am sure the chest infection and the antibiotics have a lot to do with it. We intend to go to Age UK for your stretch exercise class, but we shall see. Coronavirus has exploded in Italy and there are some cases in the UK as well. Experts believe it could get bad here too and you would be in the vulnerable category for which the virus can be dangerous. How to keep you safe? Frequent and thorough hand washing is a recommendation. You are so awkward with your hands, however, that your hand washing would not pass muster. Thankfully we have plenty of antibacterial gel for you.

Tuesday 17th March 2020

It's been quite a few days since I recorded anything but you have not had the best time. The infection has not fully gone yet. Despite this, you cannot take any more antibiotics given you had two full weeks of them. The infection and the fear of Coronavirus have set you back even further. You now are completely unable to understand the simplest instructions and you seem miserable and angry all the time. Adri has been working from home for a few days now and he has noticed how difficult and tiring it is to take care of you. He realises that we need support quickly and he rang Puneet to try to expedite the search for an alternative. The government has advised that the over seventies should self-isolate and avoid social contact for up to four months. This may mean four months indoors with you, alone. I have already stopped taking you to classes and I have cancelled your Tuesday Vintage Club. This makes the day very long indeed, especially as you no longer enjoy doing anything. That leaves you with twenty-four hours of nothing, wandering up and down the house like a lost soul. You seem totally unable to relax. It is really painful and disconcerting to watch you. You are like someone who cannot settle anywhere and cannot enjoy anything. We still go for a little walk every day, ensuring we do not come into close contact with other people and we try to avoid touching anything while outdoors. On our return home, I wash my hands and you use the antibacterial gel. Truc has been working from home for the past few days as well. So there are four of us in the house, which makes this less unbearable. Adri and Truc will be moving out soon and I dread the prospect of these four months isolation alone with you. I suggested today that you need to try to find an interest, anything at all that can keep you occupied for a bit. You said you may try drawing. We will see.

Wednesday 18th March 2020

Although we have nothing to do all day we got up at 8.30 a.m. because you woke up at eight o'clock in a panic, screaming, "Help me! Help me!" and trying to stand up. However, once you were on your feet you sat on the bed again, asking, "Can I lie down with you?"

"Of course, my love. Lie down and I will tuck you in." Twenty minutes later, you are up again like a jack in the box. It is now 10.30 a.m. Since you had breakfast you have sat down on your chair three or four times, then got up again saying you do not feel well. You have recently switched to sitting on the sofa next to me, which is really sweet. I gave you the newspaper with the page open at the crossword. You looked at it but put it back on the table. This morning whilst brushing your teeth you said that you are afraid of me. I asked you why, given that I look after you, have never hurt you and would never hurt you. You replied that you did not know. You have picked up the crossword again and are trying to get the paper off the clipboard. You look so lost and uneasy and I feel so much tenderness for you. You are like a scared animal who hits out at everything, as you see danger everywhere. Have you really gone forever, or will I once again have a glimpse of my beautiful, funny, kind, loving, exciting man? Somehow I doubt it. And this breaks my heart.

11.00 a.m.: I am looking at you. You have reached for the tonic water, the chewing gum and the TV control on your side table, but you do not pick anything up. You then touch your chin and stare into space. Your phone starts to play classical music, the alarm we've set to remind you to take your tablets. I tell you to take three tablets from the pill box in your pocket. You do not seem to compute this, so Adri comes to help you.

12.30 p.m.: We're back from our walk, during which we carefully avoided people. For the last six hundred metres you could hardly walk. I had to hold on to you and stop every hundred steps or so. Once we were back indoors I said you should sit down, but you seemed frozen to the spot, just inside the door behind the sofa. "Come on, Jim. Hold my hands and then I can guide you to the sofa."

"Leave me alone." I walked away from you and entered the kitchen to calm down and you followed me in there.

"Jim, you are exhausted and could hardly make it home. Why don't you sit down?"

"Shall I make you a cup of tea?" you ask.

"No, Jim. You sit down and I will make you a cup of tea." Eventually you sat down.

2.00 p.m.: I have prepared pasta for our lunch and ask where you would like to eat it. You point towards your armchair. So I ask you to sit down. You seem to be struggling as usual, so I take one of your hands to help you. You use the other hand to push me away. I come close to you and ask you to sit down by yourself then but you lash out at me. You punched me right on my face. Adri was seated on the small sofa working on his computer and saw the whole interaction. He jumped up, pushed you down on the armchair and shouted, "If you ever do this again to Mum, I am not going to talk to you, ever again. You are destroying this family. You need to change your behaviour. It is unacceptable." You cower and your face is full of shock and fear. Adri goes upstairs to take a call and you ask to be let out of the house. I explain that because of the virus you cannot go out on your own, as you are vulnerable. You do not seem to understand and are trying to get out so I lock the door. This brings tears to your eyes and I feel so desperately sad. I cuddle you and I say you cannot behave like this and expect to be treated with love and affection. Adri comes down the stairs a few minutes later with open arms. He comes towards you and says, "Dad, give me a hug. I am sorry for the way I behaved. You should not hit Mum but my reaction was terrible. It will never happen again. But you need to stop hitting Mum." You flinch and say you are afraid. I say,

"You are the aggressor, not us."

Thursday 19th March 2020

11.00 a.m.: You are sitting in your chair trying to sleep but, as usual, you are restless. You slept for only three hours last night, following a very sad and eventful evening. After the episode with Adri you seemed even more needy than usual and kept asking for hugs. We sat together on the sofa holding hands and fell asleep for an hour. When you woke up, you looked scared and kept mumbling. It was clear that you were deeply confused as you did not know who either Adri or I was. This had never happened before. I burst into tears, hugged you and told you that I will never react badly to you again. You spent the rest of the evening dozing. At 9.30 p.m. you started asking when we were going to bed. I said we should wait until 10.30 p.m. or you would wake up too early. We went up at 10.30 p.m., but it was apparent that it was going to be a very bad night. You fell asleep for half an hour then woke up needing the toilet, as you had refused to go before getting into bed. You went to the toilet but could not do it. You called me and I tried to help you, without success. Back in the bedroom, I helped you lie down. I lifted your legs onto the bed and covered you up. Five minutes later the whole process began again. This continued until 4.00 a.m. when I gave you your Sinemet tablets, in the hope they would help you to sleep. You eventually dropped off at 4.30 a.m. Three hours later you awoke, full of angst and anguish.

1.50 p.m.: You are sleeping on the sofa after eating your lunch. I look at you and an overwhelming sadness takes hold of me. I start crying at the thought that I will never again share a witty remark with you, that we will never again have a conversation about anything other than your essential needs. The thought that you will never again look at me with love, lust and respect also fills me with despair. Oh, how I wish I could have stopped time in January 2019, our last proper holiday, in Valencia. We were such a happy, close couple and people who saw us together often remarked on this. I was so happy and grateful to have found you.

2.10 p.m.: You wake up and I give you a hug but cannot stop crying. You ask me why I am crying and add, "Don't worry, we will be okay." Oh, how I hope this is so.

Friday 27th March 2020

We have now spent our first week of isolation because of COVID-19. We cannot even go for walks any longer. The weather has been nice, so we have been able to go into the garden. You seem to be terrified of COVID-19, whilst not fully understanding that we cannot go out and why this is. You always ask, "What are we going to do today?" And I reply,

"The usual. We may do some exercises indoors. We may read, watch TV, draw, play games, whatever you wish to do, my love." But, of course, you will not be doing anything at all. You will just wander around the house, angry, upset and confused. Isolation means that you cannot go for walks, you cannot attend your classes and you cannot meet up with your mates, and this lack of stimuli has plunged you into a hellish nothingness, where we are unable to reach you.

No one can understand you when you talk now. You seem unable to construct a simple, intelligible sentence. You mumble continually but what you say cannot be understood. Once in a while, between the mumblings I can hear 'excuse me' or 'help me'. The terror of Coronavirus and the restrictions of self-isolation stop you from functioning, even at the most basic level. The other day you asked me, "Can you show me where the toilet is, as I am new here?" You seem unhappy all the time. You keep asking to be set free, as you do not seem to understand that we are self-isolating for you in particular, as you are vulnerable. You never laugh or even smile any longer. You, who used to be so self-mocking. You had such a beautiful laugh and could find humour in most situations.

Wednesday 1st April 2020

The past few days of self-isolation have brought us a few moments of hope and love but many periods of distress and misery. When we did karaoke singing you joined in heartily, especially when we sang Frank Sinatra's songs. On one occasion we sang our two favourite Neil Young's songs - 'Four Strong Winds' and 'Already One'. While we were singing 'Already One', you bent down and kissed me on the mouth, with love. Clearly reminiscent of better times. Your nighttime periods of wakefulness have become more manic and you often seem in a state of panic. You stand up, walk to the bedroom door, open it and look out into the corridor with great apprehension, before coming back to the bed. You hover near the bed for five to ten minutes and then sit very precariously on the edge. There is always the danger that you may miss the bed and fall on the floor. You stare in front of you for a few minutes. You ask me for help to lie down and five minutes later we are back to square one. During the day it is very much the same. You cannot stay either sitting or standing for long periods and you are always attempting to either get up or sit down. When you struggle to stand up from the chair you ask for help. This might take place twenty times a day. The physiotherapist suggested that getting up from the chair should form part of your daily exercises and you should practise and do it by yourself. When I remind you of this, however, you tend to moan. And, at times, you get so frustrated that you cry. More often, the anger and adrenalin help you to get up. You may then wander up and down the length of the house, then try to sit down again. I say 'try' because you seriously struggle to sit down and usually I need to instruct you, help you and guide you. You seem to be talking nonsense most of the time. You mention being employed. You talk about bosses, police and papers to sign, but your most recurrent theme is that you are homeless and without a penny. When I try to assure you that this is your home and you can have everything you need, you tend to get angry.

9.40 p.m.: You walk in front of me whilst I am watching TV and ask what time we are going to bed. "We will go at about 10.30, my love. In the meantime, sit down and watch TV or read something."

"That is not fair. I need a bed to sleep in. I cannot sleep with the light on."

"You will not sleep with the light on. When we go to bed we will turn the light off." And you continue to wander aimlessly with an expression of anguish on your face. I find it impossible to connect and have a sensible conversation with you.

Tuesday 7th April 2020

Over the past three days you have sunk even deeper within yourself. Even Adri struggles to reach you. Two nights ago you woke up to go to the toilet as usual. From the bedroom I heard water falling on the floor. I came to investigate and you were peeing with your pants on, onto the floor, between the corridor and the entrance to the toilet. Once you had finished, you started walking back towards the bedroom. "Jim, let me clean you up, or you will spread pee all over the house," I said.

"Go away," you replied, while looking at me vacantly and terrified at the same time. I tried to hold you where you were but you pushed me away quite hard. Adri came to help and after a lot of coaxing and pleading, we managed to clean you up before you returned to the bedroom. However, this incident must have caused you additional distress as you would not allow me near you, so I went to the spare room. You spent the next three hours opening and closing our bedroom door and turning the light on and off. You then went to the toilet again and the same scene ensued. Thankfully, this time you were very close to the bowl and your pee ended up on the toilet floor. You always knew where to go for a piss or a shit, even if you could not sit yourself down. Given these latest incidents I am not sure this is still the case. Let's hope this is just a blip, or I will need to be totally vigilant to ensure you do not do it on the carpet. I also know that you will not accept a nappy. Last night, you were totally anti-me and would not listen to anything I said. Adri had to intervene and it took him a couple of hours to get you back into bed. After that the night was not particularly bad. However, this morning you started the day totally paranoid. "I have been turfed out," you said as soon you got up, which would be funny if it wasn't so distressing for you and given that we need to lock the front door to stop you from going out.

We came downstairs at approximately 9.00 a.m. and since then you have been on a loop. You walk from the back door, which is open going out onto the garden, to the front door. You touch the handle, realise it is locked and return to the back door. You refused to eat your breakfast and are not responding to anything either Adri or I say. The alarm on your phone just played for your eleven o'clock tablets but when I mentioned this, you stared at me blankly. You switch between sheer panic and complete apathy. The sadness of it all. COVID-19 has taken away the little bit of livelihood you had left. The terror of the virus and the feeling of being kept prisoner, as you are not allowed to go outside, have caused a short circuit in your brain. You have just sat down on the rocking chair because you are obviously tired and need a rest. I called your name as I wanted you to sit in the more comfortable armchair or sofa, but you did not acknowledge me.

11.25 a.m.: I'm in the garden as it is a glorious day. I can see you peeping through the door, so I come in and ask you if you want to join me. You respond by crossing your fingers, touching your chest and saying, "It hurts." I do not understand what you mean, but I say,

"I am your wife. I love you, please come outside." You just walk away. My heart is broken and I cannot stop crying. Adri told me yesterday,

"You need to stop treating Dad as if he is still your husband. That person is gone. He is very sick and you should not get hurt at what he says or react badly to his behaviour. Of course, you need to point out to him that he cannot be aggressive. Other than that, just try to distract him to take him away from whatever obsession he is concentrating on." This morning, Adri tried to talk to you in his usual calm and warm way. He kept asking, "Are you all right, Dad?" You did not acknowledge or respond to him and he had to admit that we cannot reach you, whichever technique we use. I think he is very sad and hurt that you do not respond to him either. I am used to it but Adri is not and I feel pain and anguish for him, for you, for all of us.

Easter Sunday 12th April 2020

You and I were in the garden. Truc came out and said that a blackbird had nested in one of our shrubs. I looked and sure enough, among the branches was the nest with a baby bird in it. I mentioned this to you but you barely acknowledged it. When I saw a beautiful butterfly I pointed it out to you and you smiled. That made me cry. You used to be fascinated by butterflies. You would show them to me with childlike enchantment and a beautiful smile. Birds, as well, were a source of pleasure to you, both their sight and their sound. That day our garden was alive with the singing of birds but you didn't seem to hear them. I remember when you pointed out the Pied Wagtail dancing around on the streets of Feltham. It really looked as though it was dancing a very intricate dance on the road - not flying, just bouncing on the road. We later discovered that it is called 'Ballerina' in Italian. How fitting! You liked the freedom that birds have. Soaring high into the sky, away from everything and everybody. Flying was indeed the superpower you craved. You often had dreams about flying but they turned into nightmares when your wings would no longer work and you would plunge to the ground, unable to stop. These dreams were quite recurrent and you would wake up in a sweat. When we first arrived in Italy you discovered the little birds my father, who was a hunter, kept in cages to use as bait when he went hunting. You were so outraged and wanted to set them free. I really had to get angry with you to stop you, because that was not your choice to make. You thought it was such a cruelty. You experienced the same outrage when we took Adri to Chessington Zoo. We came to the orangutan enclosure, where a couple were holding on to each other and looking out to the crowds with such sad eyes that you said you felt guilty just being there. All day today you have appeared terrified and highly disorientated. You keep saying that you want to go home. I think 'home' for you is a place where you are no longer afraid, a place where we used to be happy. You are so sad all the time. I hope this hell does not last long for you.

Saturday 18th April 2020

1.45 p.m.: You have just woken up after a two hour sleep. Last night you slept for less than two hours. You were completely 'absent' but kept mumbling. In spite of being exhausted, you were very active and energetic, getting yourself in and out of bed without help. At 6.00 a.m. I went into the spare room and managed to get a couple of hours sleep. I am sure you did not, because when I came back to the bedroom you had pulled a lot of your clothes out of the wardrobe in an attempt to dress yourself.

On Tuesday you had a second confrontation with Adri. You had asked me to take you to the toilet. I had pulled your trousers down and managed to get you sitting on the toilet after a lot of effort and persuasion. After a minute or so I asked if you had finished and you said you had. When you stood up I could see you had not done anything, so I asked you to try again or we would have to come back shortly and go through the whole procedure again. I was trying to get you to sit back down on the bowl when you snarled at me and pushed me away. I was so angry that I needed to get out of the toilet to calm myself down. I pulled the door shut behind me and you started banging on it. I then opened the door, bent down to pull your trousers up and you punched me right on the chin. I still have a blue bruise, because you caught me whilst I was leaning into you. Adri was in the living room working and jumped up angrily. He pulled your pants up, lifted you up and sat you down in your chair. "That is unacceptable. You cannot hit Mum like that. She is only trying to help you. What have you become? My father would never behave like this." You were a nervous wreck and kept blubbering,

"Oh God, oh God, I am so sorry. I am ashamed."

"That is not good enough, Dad. In a couple of months, when the lockdown is finished, we will be moving out and Mum cannot look after you if you behave like this. Do you understand?" Adri said. You continued to snivel and kept apologising but I was still in shock. Then I looked at you and my heart melted again. How tragic your life is, my love. The rest of the week has been a total nightmare. You are living in a completely different reality, where nothing makes sense, where we cannot reach you. There have been a few moments when you've given me a hug and I feel you are still 'there', still in love. But those moments are rare. From my perspective, I am already grieving my beautiful, loving, kind man and I resent this version I now have. The tragedy is that because you are so antagonistic and aggressive, even after lockdown I know I could not put you into a care home. They would have to restrain you when you lash out and I cannot allow that to happen, even though I would understand why they acted that way. I love you but you manage to make me so angry that I end up shouting at you and saying awful things, which I regret as soon as I have uttered them.

Sunday 17th May 2020

God I dislike you! You are fast asleep in your armchair after trying to 'escape' and managing to get down the road. I truly thought about letting you go and possibly endangering your safety, given that you do not understand social distancing and you are mostly unaware of the dangers.

It has been a bad day. Dr Tai has prescribed a new tablet for dementia. He never said that you had dementia but I recently rang him to ask if there was anything that could help you and he prescribed this new drug. I thought I could see a slight improvement a few days after you had started taking it but today you are as bad as ever. We were outside in the garden and you woke up in a panic and a foul mood. You looked at me and said that I was a fat cow and a cunt. I stopped acknowledging you. You started mumbling and then screamed "Help!" in a rather loud voice. Adri heard and ran outside. He tried to talk to you, to reason with you in his usual understanding and relaxed tone, which I admire so much but am unable to emulate. But you were raging and – unusually - you took it out on him. You called him a coward and told him to fuck off. I was mortified and really hurt that you should speak like that to our son. Adri turned to me and said,

"I don't know what to do, Mum." I replied.

"Do not worry, my love. Go back to your work and leave him here. He will calm down if I don't acknowledge him." As soon as Adri was back inside the house, tears came to my eyes. I turned to you and said, "I am used to your nastiness but I will not stand by and watch you hurt our son. Do you understand me?" You seemed to realise what you had done and apologised, adding that you would never do it again. I was so riled, however, that I could not be appeased and kept saying horrible things to you. "You are a nasty piece of work, with no kindness within you. You are not my husband and I am ashamed to be your wife."

Adri and Truc will move into their new home at the end of the month and may not be able to come and stay until the lockdown is over. This terrifies me. The thought of being in the house just with you, twenty-four hours a day, fills me with dread.

Tuesday 2nd June 2020

9.20 a.m.: I cannot continue like this. I am living with a seriously deranged individual. I thought the new tablets had at last reduced your aggression because, when you have fits of temper, you seem to realise you have done something wrong almost immediately and usually apologise. Last Saturday, Adri and Truc moved out and went to live in their new home. This is obviously very sad for both of us, as Adri has been a great support, particularly during lockdown. However, it is time for them to move on and have a life away from us. This morning you were very agitated from the moment you woke up. You said that life is shit and reacted angrily whilst brushing your teeth, hurling the toothbrush into the sink as you struggled to wash the toothpaste from around your mouth. I held my tongue and managed to get you ready without further upset. I prepared your breakfast, as usual, but you shouted, "You can eat the porridge yourself. I do not want it. I have nothing." I said you should enjoy the little things in life and added,

"You have me. We have been together for forty-one years. It is hurtful to say you have nothing. And we have our son."

"Yes, Adri is the only one who cares for me."

"I care for you, too, but you need to stop being nasty to me." You barked at me. It really sounded like a bark, right in my face to frighten me. I then lost it and said that I could not live with you any longer. I rang Puneet and asked her for an emergency placement. You panicked and kept apologising. You tried to call Adri but could not succeed in dialling his number. Adri later called us and I told him what had happened. It is now 10.30 a.m. and you have been walking up and down the room for the past hour, all the time apologising. Whilst I feel sorry for you, I cannot find it in myself to be civil to you and I just ignore you. Is this cruelty or is it the normal reaction of someone who cannot take it anymore?

Saturday 6th June 2020

You are trying to fall asleep after another eventful night. It is 12.15 p.m. and I cannot stop crying because I feel I am a bully and an evil witch. Yesterday was your birthday. Adri and Truc came to visit for the first time since they moved out last Saturday. They've had very little contact with other people but more than when they were in lockdown with us, because of deliveries and installations in their new home. The weather was bad and we had to stay inside the house, at a reasonable distance from one another. Adri and Truc wore their masks. The day was going well, until you and I decided to go out into the garden for a few minutes. I was trying to help you sit down on the chair when you pounced on me and went for my neck again, which really surprised me as you had not shown aggression for many days. So I probably overreacted. I swore at you and told you that as soon as a place becomes available at a care home, you are gone. You disappeared within yourself as you normally do, then after about an hour with Adri mediating you apologised and I relented. When Adri and Truc left we were okay. We went to bed at eleven-ish and you woke up at 2.30 a.m. needing the toilet. I was helping you in a calm and soothing way but you grabbed my face and then tried to punch me. "You are a violent, evil creature. I cannot stand to be with you," I shouted. I went to the spare room and shut the door. I could hear you moving about, shifting things. After an hour or so I calmed down, felt incredible guilt and went back to our room. You had taken the majority of your clothes out of the wardrobe. You had managed to put on a shirt but obviously the trousers defeated you. I approached you gently and asked you to come to bed with me and you gladly accepted my invite. We lay down together and slept until 8.15 a.m. When you woke up I hugged you really hard and apologised. I felt so down and upset with my behaviour. And I have not recovered yet. I cannot believe I can be so evil and callous.

You are up and wandering, unable to settle. It is a rainy and cold day, so we are stuck indoors. Donna gave you a jigsaw puzzle for your birthday. It says on the box '0 to 3 years old'. How insulting. Yet, you do not seem able to do it. My beautiful, clever, sensual, exciting man. Where are you? How can I ever stop crying when I look at you and do not recognise you? Promise to self: I need to be kind and I will never get angry again. You had a little doze and woke up pointing at things on the table. I called out names of objects but you kept shaking your head. Eventually you said you did not remember.

4.30 p.m.: We had our lunch late as you slept 'til 3.00 p.m. We were at the table eating and I was still crying over our situation. You must have misunderstood my tears and said, "There will have to be consequences."

"What for?" I asked.

"Lawyers will need to be involved," you continued.

"Jim, why would we need lawyers?"

"A man is dead and someone has to pay."

"Jim, whatever you think has happened, it is only in your head. No one relevant to us has died. I am just sad, that is why I am crying." You shook your head and said,

"Cath, I am mad. Do not pay any attention to me. You should have at your side a much better man than me."

"Jim, I do not want anyone else, really. I mean it. I just want you."

When we finished eating we did the crossword together and then got up from the table. 'Morning has broken' was playing on the radio and I grabbed your hands and started dancing with you. You joined in and then we held each other really close and tight and you said, "I wish we could stay like this forever." I could have cried again but for joy this time, because I had a glimpse of your old self, even if fleeting.

Wednesday 10th June 2020

5.30 p.m.: We have had a few good days. No anger, no aggression and a lot of kissing and cuddling. Today I sat at the dining room table on a Zoom call with my colleagues. You were sitting on the sofa watching 'Flog it' on TV, which you still enjoy. My call started at 4.30 p.m. and finished at 5.10 p.m. When I entered the lounge you were no longer sat on the sofa and I realised that you were not in the house. I rushed out and looked up and down the road but I couldn't see you. I didn't know what to do. You did not have your phone with you and you are totally unaware of the need to social distance. I called Adri in a panic and he advised to stay put and await your return. After a few minutes I was frantic and called the police as you are vulnerable, unaware and would really be at risk if you caught the virus. Whilst on the phone to the police I saw you coming around the bend towards the house. I rushed out and escorted you home. You told me that you walked to Tesco but did not go in. I asked why you left without saying anything and you told me you wanted to go to London to 'claim a bed'. I asked if you had come in close contact with anyone while out and you said that nobody made an effort to come close to you, thankfully.

Friday 12th June 2020

Yesterday was a very good day. Just after breakfast you came towards me, took my hands, told me I was beautiful and started moving to the sound of music. A Phil Collins song was playing on the radio and you looked intensely into my eyes, then put on your 'playboy' act and I burst out laughing as I used to when you dropped your lower lip and raised your eyebrow in a supposedly sexy manner. You then moved closer to me and we kissed and cuddled like we used to. You started kissing my neck and ears while I massaged your back and bum. We both took our trousers off and masturbated reciprocally. It was magic. Of course, I had to help you to take your trousers off but it was all so gentle and full of love.

I love you so much, but I can 'see' you only very seldom through the fog of Parkinson's and dementia. You have also started to forget things. Adri told us that Truc had tested positive for COVID-19. They ordered the test to ensure that they could come to see us again at the weekend without worries. Adri's test was inconclusive but Truc's was positive. This means that they cannot come to see us for at least fourteen days. I repeated this to you and explained that Adri was very concerned about us. When they came to visit for your birthday a week ago they wore masks and kept their distance but, of course, you never know. Anyhow, I was explaining this to you but you did not remember them being here wearing masks. I showed you the picture we took on the day but you still could not recall. You ask me almost every day if Adri is coming to see us. And you also ask if I am going to work. Oh, your poor jumbled up brain.

1.25 p.m.: You have just woken up, as I am writing this, and you ask, "Anyone coming today?"

Saturday 27th June 2020

We had another good week. We were friendly, companionable and enjoying a couple of dances here and there. And naturally some good, almost normal sex. Then you developed a chest infection again and were unable to stand. You became very wobbly on your legs and tended to lean backwards when standing up. We stopped all exercises and you started your antibiotics, which always knock you for six. You spent most of the day sleeping but, thankfully, there was no nastiness or aggression in you. You finished the antibiotics four days ago now and you are slowly recuperating your balance and mobility. Yesterday, however, from first thing in the morning I knew there was something wrong again, as you kept mumbling and making unintelligible sounds. When I asked what you'd said you tried to talk to me, but all that came out of your mouth was nonsense, jumbled up words that did not make any sense. You stated that I had a new man - I managed to understand this much. I responded that you must have had a bad dream, because I am clearly only with you and I want only you. You also said that there was a monster in the toilet. I asked you to come out into the garden with me but you declined. I could not relax, however, with you being indoors on your own and after twenty minutes came back in to see how you were. I found you sitting on the floor, having fallen on your bum and unable to get up. I got you back on your feet with great difficulty and you became very agitated. You were trying to say something to me that I could not decipher. This frustrated you and you showed signs of aggression for the first time in a long while. This, as usual, enraged me. You started yelling at me and quite clearly said that you will kill me. This I know you would never do, but the simple fact you could utter such violent words made me feel incensed and I shouted, "Remember that I would always win in a fight against you, mate." You then started pacing up and down the house and stopped only when I understood from your garbled words that you needed the toilet. Still not understanding anything you were trying to tell me, I rang the doctor for advice. He called back half an hour later, suggested that you may have a urine infection and prescribed a new set of antibiotics. When our neighbour finished work, she went to Asda to collect them. But by mistake they had been sent to Boots, which was closed at the time, so she could not pick them up. The doctor had advised to give you two tablets last night and then one a day. He added that if you had not improved by the following morning, i.e. today, I should call 111. With no antibiotics, you making no sense at all and constantly asking for help with everything, I was exhausted. At 8.00 p.m. I surmised you needed the toilet again and, after a monumental struggle, I managed to get you onto the bowl. You had a poo and when you had finished I asked you to hold on to the grab rail with both hands as you usually did while I cleaned your bum, but you pushed me away and walked out of the toilet with your shorts around your ankles and a soiled bum. I flushed and cleaned the bowl with the brush and when I came out you were on the floor again on your bum. I helped you up with an enormous struggle but you would not allow me to clean you and pull up your shorts. You walked away from me, still with your shorts around your ankles and shouted at me to go away. You still looked very 'absent' and we had no antibiotics to ease the infection, so I dialled 999 because I did not know what else to do. By the time the ambulance arrived you had managed to pull your shorts up but you were still soiled. The two paramedics were really nice. They took your vital signs and all was good. They asked you for the name of our cat, where and when you and I had met, my name and our address. You managed to reply correctly to all these questions. You always perform well for medical people. They asked you to allow me to clean you up, which you agreed to do and then they thought that the best way forward was to get the antibiotics and see how you went.

As it turned out, the night was not too bad, although you wet the bed for the second time ever. Thankfully, after the first time I had bought some waterproof mattress covers. However, you must have been lying on your back, as the duvet was also soaked. I changed the bedding including the duvet and we went back to sleep. We woke up at 8.00 a.m. and you were still very 'off'. Contrary to normal you had a very small breakfast and you have been trying to rest ever since. It is now 11.30 a.m. and you're sitting in your chair with your eyes shut, mouth open and such an anguished expression that you remind me of 'The Scream' by Edvard Munch. Our neighbour will try to collect your antibiotics, wherever they are, today. We are so lucky to have Donna as a neighbour. She has been an absolute star during this period. Adri rings every evening and we exchange regular messages but he is not here with us. And it is difficult for him to help, although he is a great boost to both you and me. Tomorrow he will be coming to see us. Let's hope you are better by then.

Monday 29th June 2020

8.10 p.m.: You are asleep in your chair. Adri and Truc left one hour ago, after an overnight visit. Yesterday you improved slightly and were able to say a few consecutive words that made some sense. Adri and Truc were not due until late afternoon and as the weather was bad, you suggested that we should have a game of chess. I was a bit hesitant, given that you have been struggling to even play drafts recently, but I thought as you used to love chess so much you may indeed still be able to play a bit. I set up my side of the board, in the hope that you could copy my setup. But it became apparent that we were not going to play chess. Although you were able to name all the pieces, you had no idea where to place them. And you just placed them randomly, anywhere, even across squares. Oh Tesoro, it has all gone away. Your love of chess was strong and the game gave you a lot of enjoyment. You liked to look at chess puzzles in The Guardian and work them out. You had a chess computer game, which kept you occupied for hours when there was no one you could play with. When we lived in Italy for the first four years of Adri's life, you taught anyone who was interested how to play the game. This included Mario, my student Luca, my cousin, Paolo, son of a cousin and other youngsters in the village. Mari's boyfriend at the time was Marcello and he also loved chess. So, a game was arranged for one evening in the bar. This attracted quite a number of spectators and the tension was similar to the Fisher vs Spassky World Championship final. After a tough game, you won. Yes! My most memorable game of chess, however, is the one we played the night Adri was born. My waters broke at approximately 2.30 a.m. but the contractions did not seem regular as yet. So you pulled out the chessboard after making us both a cup of tea and suggested we played a game, whilst waiting for things to develop. The hospital was only twenty minutes away, after all. We never finished that game, as the contractions became sharper and more regular within the hour, and our beautiful boy was born less than three hours later, at 6.10 a.m. on 3rd August 1982.

When Adri and Truc arrived we ate dinner and the evening was quite pleasant, even though you drifted in and out of sleep. Today, you played 'catch the ball' with Adri and tried to make conversation. I say 'tried' because it is excruciating to guess what you want to say. You did manage to communicate a couple of things. You, Adri and I did the crossword companionably, with you managing to solve quite a few clues. It always surprises me that you cannot say 'I need to go to the loo' but you can still recollect words such as bassoon, disintegrate, éclat, ennui, oxymoron, etc. It does not make sense. Where are you, my love? The man who I fell in love with, the one I could not bear to be apart from, even for short periods. I was so looking forward to our retirement together. I feel so sad, thinking that we will never have a holiday together again. Valencia, our short break in January 2019 to celebrate forty years together, will surely be our last ever, proper holiday. I need to find the strength to carry on in order to help you. You need me so badly that I resent it and this plunges me into the darkest despair. Every time I see a book with a dedication from you in it, every time I hear a song that meant anything to us I burst out crying. You are not coming back to me, that is clear and I feel such a knot in my stomach, I cannot breathe.

Tuesday 30th June 2020

3.15 p.m.: You are calm and all your vital signs are okay: blood pressure, pulse, temperature, oxygen level and you ate well, but you look totally 'absent' again. You told me that you feel fuzzy and empty. You try to talk but your voice is faint and I cannot hear what you want to say. I ask you to repeat it but you cannot do so. For the past fifteen minutes you have been obsessing about Dice. You let him out but within a couple of minutes you are trying to get him to come back in. You open the inside front door and you call him. I say, "Jim, you need to open the outside door as well, for the cat to be able to get in." You look at me as though I am talking Martian. "Jim, do you understand what I am saying?"

"I am not sure." I repeat the instruction and you still look puzzled. You look out through the outside door's glass. I then come next to you and say,

"Press the green button." You do that but Dice has no intention of coming back in, as he is quite happy in the front garden. The outer door closes automatically and I ask you to close the inside door. That leads to additional puzzlement and confusion. I close the door for you in the end. I see you disappearing before my eyes, day after day, and I am distraught for us both but I know I cannot stop it from happening.

You have been trying to read short stories, as a full novel has become impossible. But you said that even short stories are too difficult. I brought you a children's book by Anthony Horowitz and asked you to read aloud to me. You managed to read the first two paragraphs quite well but then your voice faded altogether and with it, I fear, your understanding. I feel desperate my love, my clever, lost love. What makes me cry almost all the time is the sense of loss. So complete, even though you are still with me, physically. Your presence is a constant reminder of what I have lost. The excitement of looking for the perfect holiday, the anticipation of our weekends together and what they would bring. Despair; black despair.

Sunday 5th July 2020

I know I have written that you are totally gone many times before, but over the past twenty-four hours or so we have reached another level of hopelessness and despair for both of us. You, because you have travelled to a dark place where you see me as your enemy. And me, because I have lost every hope of even a minor improvement and I feel stuck with you, without hope of getting out of this hell. When you woke up yesterday everything seemed normal and all remained okay until you had your nap at midday. You woke up at 2.00 p.m. and I said I would get lunch ready in the next half an hour. Off I went to the kitchen and you called me saying you wanted to get up from your armchair. I came to help you and you grabbed my hands and stood up. Once you were stable on your feet, I said, "Let my hands go." But you kept holding on tight. I tried to pull them away from your grip but you yanked me back and fell on your bum between the sofa and the toilet, with your back against the door. I helped you up, saying that you need to be careful. As soon as you were on your feet, you moved to the front door and tried to get out. "Jim, you know you cannot go out by yourself because of the virus. Let's have lunch and then we can go for a walk together," I said. I was holding your arm and you grabbed the chains around my neck and started pulling. I was really afraid for a second or so. Anyway, the chains broke and because you were yanking so hard, you fell again. I locked the front door and got you back up on your feet.

I rang Adri as I was distressed and he said that he would come over. You fell into a stupor and sat on the sofa with a fixed stare. I was crying with great sobs. Adri and Truc arrived around 4.00 p.m. Adri squeezed your shoulders with affection and said he knows you are not conscious of what you are doing, as it is the illness making you act the way you do. Truc is still coughing, even though they both tested negative after she had the virus, therefore she wore a mask and went straight upstairs. Adri turned the TV on and you sat calmly on the sofa with him, watching a football match. As you appeared okay, Adri said they would return home but to call if we needed anything. You had a nap as soon as they left, from 6.00 until 7.00 p.m. When you woke up, I went to prepare dinner and helped you to sit at the table. You had a good helping of chilli con carne and then had your Cornetto ice cream. I helped you back on your feet to return to the sofa but you looked possessed. Your eyes were wide open and you didn't seem to see me. You walked straight to the front door and said I should let you go. "If you want to go for a walk, I will come with you." I took hold of your hand to help you with the front steps but you pushed me away and tried to step out into our driveway by yourself. Obviously, you lost your balance and fell in the front garden on your bum again, with your back against the door. I tried to help you up but you started screaming,

"Help! Somebody help!" You shouted the same thing to anyone going passed our house. People asked if we needed help but I explained that you were not well. I called the ambulance as I did not know what else to do once again. The paramedics helped you back into the house and checked you out. They said they should take you to the hospital for an assessment but added that you should go on your own because of COVID-19. I asked you if you wanted to go to hospital and you replied, "No." I told the paramedics I could not do this to you. I could not let you go on your own to the hospital. They said it was my choice and advised me to ask our GP for a full review, as your behaviour may not be caused by an infection but by the progression of Parkinson's or Dementia. The rest of the evening was uneventful. We went to bed at 11.00 p.m. and you woke up at 1.00 a.m. for the toilet, which unfortunately led to another crisis. I went back to the bedroom from the toilet, while you went downstairs.

You had taken your vest off, so you were naked and although it was 22.5 degrees in the room you were shivering. I tried to put your bathrobe on but you started shouting "Help! You want to kill me." I begged you to come back upstairs to bed but you replied that you were afraid of the other man upstairs. You also mentioned that there were four lads in the house.

"Jim, there is nobody in the house except you and me," I assured you. You started shouting again, so I went back upstairs. At approximately 4.30 a.m., I heard a bang. I rushed downstairs and you had taken a saucepan to have a pee in. This had then slipped out of your hands and some urine had spilled on the floor. I cleaned it up and managed to persuade you to put your bathrobe on, but you still refused to come upstairs and it was now 6.00 a.m. I kept climbing up and down the stairs every ten minutes until 7.00 a.m., still begging you to come to bed to get some sleep. You said you would try to have a sleep on the sofa. I put a blanket over you and went upstairs again. Twenty minutes later you called me and when I came back down I could smell shit. You agreed to come upstairs for a little rest. You went to the toilet and indeed there was some shit on your bathrobe. I cleaned you up and tucked you up in bed. You woke up at 9.30 a.m., jumped out of the bed, still with 'stary' eyes and went downstairs, stark-naked. When I tried to get near you, you screamed.

11.00 a.m.: I asked you to get dressed and then we could have breakfast. You screamed, "Leave me alone, fuck face."

12.30 p.m.: A 360 degree turn around. You allowed me to dress you and we had a late breakfast. Then you needed a poo, again. Obviously you have a bit of diarrhoea and, to my horror, I noticed that your bum was getting sore again. I have been applying creams to your bum and have used some gauze to stop the soreness and it had improved. But after being soiled with shit during the night, it looked very raw again. I gently applied some cream and after I pulled your trousers up, you gave me a big cuddle and a kiss. I asked, "What goes on in that brain of yours?"

"God knows," you replied. "We had a bad start this morning but we are going to be okay," you reassured me. You seem almost normal now but for how long? I swing between pity and indifference, and between love and hatred. Even my emotions are all fucked up. And I am physically and emotionally exhausted, with no end in sight.

3:30pm: "When are we going home?" you asked.

"We are home, Jim."

"But we need to be off duty."

"We are both retired and are always off duty."

"Why are we working then?"

"We are not working. We can just sit down and relax, or do whatever we like," I tried to reassure you.

"I have never been so tired."

"You are tired because you did not sleep during the night. Have a rest and a sleep, if you want." You still look puzzled and I suggest we turn on the TV. This seems to grab your attention for a few minutes. We are definitely not out of the woods yet. We never will be.

3.42 p.m.: You are distressed again and keep asking to go home. You then say you are going to have a rest but you stare at the TV. I have just helped you to sit down and you say in your pleading tone, almost crying, "Help me."

"I am helping you. I am here to take care of you. Relax and have a nap."

Tuesday 7th July 2020

2.57 a.m.: You woke up twenty minutes ago, I presume to go to the toilet, and you have been shouting ever since, "Help me. Help me. 195 Rochester Avenue." Whenever I came near you, you shouted louder. So I left you upstairs and I am now downstairs. Yesterday, your behaviour and remarks confirmed that your illness has progressed to yet another stage, as you asked me "What shall I call you?" When I told you that I was your wife, you seemed to snap out and said, "Yes, you are my Cath." However, you later asked me, "At what time are you going to bed?" I said we would go up, as usual, at around 11.00 p.m. "Together?" you replied. I explained that we have slept together for the past forty-one years, as we are married.

3.02 a.m.: You are now quiet but I can still hear you pacing on the landing. Finally, at 5.30 a.m. you went to the toilet and I convinced you to come to bed. You slept until 8.30 a.m.

After breakfast, you started pacing up and down. You do this now, usually up to 12.00 p.m. and then you fall asleep in your armchair, exhausted, until approximately 2.00 p.m. I reminded you that two of my friends were coming to see me, just for one hour, at 12.30. I told you that due to you being vulnerable, you need to keep well away from them and, ideally, you should remain indoors while we sit outside in the garden. This change in routine must have upset you, because you continued pacing until they arrived. You were at the front door when they rang the bell and I had to nudge you out of the way to allow them to get passed you. We then went out to the garden and I came back in to ask if you wanted to sit in your armchair and have a rest. You declined, so I let you be. I went back outside but you started banging on the door to the garden and dropped a few things on the floor inside the house. I checked that you were safe and went back out but you kept banging on the door saying, "Hello, help me." As Rachel and Sue were leaving you stood at the door, blocking the way. I asked you to move aside but you did not budge and screamed that I was trying to kill you. When I managed to shift you enough to the side for them to shuffle passed, you elbowed Rachel in her lower back. I do not know what to do with you.

Your aggression, your terror and your lack of understanding. At times I can still see your sweet, gentle nature through this entanglement of emotions but it is becoming more and more rare. After they left, I helped you to your chair and you fell asleep. You woke up after an hour and picked up your glass for a drink. You spilled it all over yourself and blamed me. When I tried to change your clothes, you again accused me of trying to kill you. I succeeded in changing your shirt but you would not let me do anything else and the lower part of your vest and your trousers were still soaking wet. Every time I come near you, you panic and shout. I am so sad, lonely, desperate and terrified for you and me both. I asked Puneet for help again. Can someone help, please? I need a break. I do not want to shirk my responsibilities but surely Social Services should be able to provide some support? Adri will come over tomorrow to give me a break.

Thursday 9th July 2020

10.00 a.m.: Adri has just left. He arrived yesterday morning and stayed overnight. While you were eating your breakfast, you asked me if I was your supervisor. That brought tears to my eyes again. When you want something now you call out, 'Hello, hello' rather than 'Cath'. This is the most painful sign that you are sliding away into a void. You still recognise Adri all the time, thankfully, and you seem to be pleasant to him. But when you are stressed or afraid you forget, briefly, who I am. When you eventually come back to me, you say that I am your Cath. You seem to be getting worse by the day. Yesterday was a very trying day and Adri could see for himself how much physical and emotional strain I am under to keep you safe. We called Puneet at Social Services again and begged her for help. I hope this emergency response comes about soon. I am adamant that you need a break from me and I know I must have a break from you. You take up all my time and sap my energy, both physically and mentally. It takes me fifteen minutes to help you sit down and two minutes later you start trying to push yourself up on the armrest to stand up again. When you cannot achieve this by yourself, which is most of the time, you cry out for help to get you up. This goes on for the majority of the day and I only have a break when you take a nap. You also talk to me all the time. I understand almost nothing of what you say, so I spend my time asking, 'Can you say that again? Can you raise your voice, please? I cannot understand what you mean.' I cannot pretend to not hear you because you 'demand' my attention. I crave grown up, normal conversation. At one point yesterday Adri wondered if you may have caught COVID-19 with the unusual effects of brain swelling and hallucinations, as reported in The Guardian, because he could not understand how you could undergo such quick deterioration. The more realistic possibility is that you may have some sort of infection again. You have had so many in the past months and each one seems to take something else away from you. A nurse came to the house yesterday to do a blood test and I need to get a urine sample and send it to the doctor for analysis. In a perverse sort of way I hope that you do have an infection and that, therefore, there is a possibility of improvement, otherwise I have to accept this 'you' as permanent. I do not think I can cope if you are as you are now, forever. In fact, I am sure I cannot cope. Help. Please someone help me.

11.00 a.m.: You have just woken up and you are terrified. I can see the fear in your eyes and you confirm this. "I am afraid."

"There is nothing to be afraid of, Jim. We are at home and we are totally safe," I say. The alarm on your phone plays music, reminding you to take your tablets. I get them from the dispenser and hand them to you. You ask,

"Shall I put them in my mouth?"

"Yes, please. Then get some water and swallow." When my eyes fill with tears again, you add,

"Don't cry, you will be all right. You are clever and I will get better."

"Yes, we will be okay," I say. "You will get better." You break my heart, my love. Do you realise what you have become and do you want to improve, or are these words spoken at random?

3.20 p.m.: You fell asleep again, straight after taking your eleven o'clock tablets. You woke up at 2.00 p.m. and it was an awful struggle to get you on your feet and to the dining table. You had a wee in the bottle because you could not face the walk to the toilet. You had a decent lunch and seemed calm but then said you were exhausted and needed to rest. You fell asleep again at 3.10 p.m.

8.15 p.m.: You just had your dinner and I cannot find it within me to be nice to you. I will take care of you but I do not believe that I will be able to show you any love and affection ever again. You woke up at 4.00 p.m. and said that you wanted to go for a walk. When I helped you up from your armchair you were very shaky, so I questioned the feasibility of going for a walk. You became agitated and I agreed to a short walk to the park and back again. We set off for the park and then turned around to come home. On arrival at our front door you refused to come in and said I was trying to kill you. You started walking away from the house, so I followed you to ensure you were safe. Seven hundred metres into your walk, you stopped dead and were unable to move either backward or forward. I didn't know what to do and I could not get you home by myself so I rang the police for help. I didn't want to call the ambulance again, as I did not want to waste their time. When the police arrived you accused me of being violent to you and said you did not want to come home with me. The police called the ambulance anyway. When the paramedics arrived you proceeded to tell them as well that I am bad towards you, I steal your money and I am violent. This was all taking place in the street. Sue, the lady you are friendly with, also stopped to watch and talked to you. There were about ten people around us. All without masks, including the paramedics. So much for shielding.

The paramedics got you home and said they would not take you to the hospital, as they feel it is just the dementia getting worse, rather than a medical emergency. They did, however, say that since accusations of violence had been made they had to follow it up. This is adding insult to injury. Not only are you the aggressor but you accuse me of it. The person who cares for you twenty-four hours a day. I feel so mortified and sad. This also means that I will never be able to take you for a walk again, as I cannot call the emergency services every time you act up. I feel trapped with no way out. Adri offered to stay with you at least one day per week to give me a break. I also contacted Harrie, your ex-carer to see if she can be with you for six hours a day, one day a week. She told me she is very busy but she will try to sort something out. This is an expensive luxury now that I am not working but given that Social Services are totally unable or unwilling to help, I need to do something or I will end up in a mental home. All Puneet has offered me in the past has been a carer for half an hour at a time to carry out specific tasks, such as wash or feed you. This is useless to me, as I never know when you will wake up and when you will eat your meals. What I need is someone to keep you company for a few hours so that I can have time for myself and recharge my batteries.

Friday 17th July 2020

3.00 p.m.: I am outside in the garden, as it is a glorious day, while you are indoors watching a football match. You did not want to come out and until we have a ramp, which will make the garden more accessible for you, I am not going to insist. It has become a gigantic effort to get you in and out of the garden now. Last Thursday night, exactly one week ago - the day after the paramedics arrived to rescue you - I slept in the spare room, because I didn't want to be near you after what you said about me to anyone who would listen. Obviously, I kept the door open so that I could hear you. I helped you in and out of bed four times but you managed to go to the toilet by yourself. The next morning you woke up screaming, “Help me! Help me!” I rushed to the bedroom and you told me to fuck off. I left you, naked, in the bedroom and went downstairs. Twenty minutes later you followed me. I got your clothes and dressed you but without showering you or brushing your teeth. Oh well, I felt sure that you could do without for one day. Puneet called to say that we could have a carer for ten hours per week, to be spread out as I like. At last, after almost seven months, some help. I am so pleased that I could jump with joy. Just as well, as Harrie said that she is not available.

I kept the front door locked as I cannot let you go out, given your weakness. You tried the front door and asked, “When can you let me free? Why am I a prisoner?” Adri advised that I should respond to you only when you are polite and well behaved, in order to reinforce positive behaviour. However, that is easier said than done, as I feel I need to watch you like a hawk to avoid you falling. And, of course, you would blame me if you did fall. Alessandra came to visit and you behaved impeccably and 'normally'. You were polite and interested in what she was saying, making appropriate remarks at the appropriate time. On Saturday morning you woke up after a good night but you were very confused. After breakfast you fell asleep and woke up terrorised, fearing for your life and asking for your freedom. The front door was still locked and you kept trying to open it. We later managed a quasi-normal evening. On Sunday, Adri and Truc visited and cooked a nice meal for the four of us. At one point, we were all in the garden when you decided that you wanted to go back in. I helped you, as I usually do, but you flopped to the ground. It almost seemed as though you let yourself drop down. Adri helped you up and took you inside. Adri and Truc stayed the night and left at 1.00 p.m. on the Monday. After your lunch, you fell asleep and when you woke up you were agitated, confused and totally incapacitated again. I tested your oxygen, your pulse, your temperature and your blood pressure. The first three were okay but your blood pressure was very high – 190/89. I tried to call the doctor but got no answer. I then called 111, who told me they were going to send paramedics to the house. I explained that the paramedics had been to the house three times in so many weeks, but the operator assured me that it is not a problem. The same pair of paramedics who came to the house the first time arrived soon after and they were visibly pissed off. I had to ask them to put masks on, as they were without them. They took your blood pressure again and told me that I should worry only if it is over 200. They then managed to get through to the doctor, who said that your blood tests did not reveal anything serious - just a bit of anaemia, which can be treated with iron tablets. The paramedics left saying that if I need help to get you off the floor, as you seem to flop down quite regularly, to call them. On Thursday, the GP rang to say that you had a very bad urine infection again. He will prescribe another course of antibiotics. I could have yelled with joy, as this explained your total collapse and meant that, therefore, you should improve once the infection is cured. All day long you are in serious danger of falling everywhere and I need to steady you every time you take a step. When you try to stand up, I need to use all my strength to get you upright, at the expense of my own back.

At 7.00 p.m., following a visit to the toilet, you flopped down to the floor. Due to the pain in my back, I was unable to get you up. I put some cushions behind your back to keep you comfortable, while I called Donna for help. Both Donna and Leanne came to help pick you up off the floor and onto the sofa. Two hours later, you were sitting on the sofa watching TV and said that you wanted to get up. When I came close in order to help you, you started screaming, "Donna! Leanne! Help me!" You continued like this for fifteen minutes, before I called Adri to see if he could get through to you. He asked you to stop screaming and, like magic, you stopped. The next day, Wednesday, Adri was going to come over for the day to give me a break. When I tried to get you out of bed, you collapsed onto the floor again. I put some cushions behind your back and propped you up against the bed, whilst waiting for Adri to arrive. He had told me that he was half an hour away. When he arrived, he helped you up, then went to get your antibiotics and iron tablets. I do hope they start working or, practically, I cannot take care of you. You seem to be falling all the time and I cannot help you up by myself, due to a pulled muscle in my back. Yesterday, the carer came to the house for four hours and I was so pleased to be free of you, it almost felt like physical pleasure. Today is your third day of antibiotics and you seem a bit better. How long for, I do not know. It seems that you are unable to shake off infections, as you get one after another. It has been like that for the past six months or so. It is now evening and we are watching TV. Rather, I am watching TV and you are sitting next to me, worried and confused. "How long do we have to wait here?"

"Gioia, we are not waiting for anything. We are just watching TV and having a chat before we go to bed." A few minutes later, I notice out of the corner of my eye that you are crying. "What's wrong, Jim?"

"I want to be normal again," you sob. Oh my love. I hug you so hard and hold you tight. Comments like these break my heart.

Saturday 18th July 2020

It was not too bad a night, apart from the usual apprehension on your trips to the toilet. We have just had a food delivery and you are in the front room with the newspapers, while I wipe down and store the shopping. You start crying out, "Hello. Hello." I walk towards you and ask,

"What is it, Jim? Please read the papers while I finish putting away the shopping."

"When are we going home?" you ask.

"We are home." Even when you are reasonably calm, I am not sure how present you are. I should take some comfort from the fact that you no longer fall to the ground every time you stand up. But your poor brain has shrunk to almost nothing.
4.00 p.m.: I went out to the garden, leaving you indoors in your armchair with the newspapers and the TV on, as you are still very wobbly. I did not think I could have managed to get you out, then back in. I also left you with a bell you could ring so that you could call me if you needed anything. Over the past half hour, you have rung the bell three times. "Can I come out with you?"

"I would love you to join me but you are not very steady on your legs yet and I could not pick you up if you fell," I said. You are now standing holding on to your armchair watching a film. Let's see how long you last before you call me again.

Sunday 19th July 2020

10.15 a.m.: I find myself crying again. For you, for us and for the prison we are both in. Yesterday, late afternoon cricket was on TV. It was live after such a long time and I thought you would be delighted, as you love cricket. You more or less love all sports. Playing and watching them, both live and on TV. We used to watch Adri playing football and that was such an enjoyment for us both. We would not have missed it for the world. At times, the cold and dampness on the side-line was dreadful and your back would get really sore but that was nothing compared with the pleasure we got. When you watched sport on TV - any sport - you were in paradise if Adri was there watching with you. You would exchange comments and jump up when there was something exciting, yelling with pleasure or disgust at whatever was happening on the screen. If Adri had not been able to join you, you would catch up with him and discuss the games, pundit like. While Adri was in Vietnam for six years, you spoke to him via Skype almost daily. Before these calls you made sure that you were fully updated on all sporting activities that had or were going to take place, to keep Adri informed but, above all, to keep that connection with him. How you loved those conversations. One example I remember particularly was in Adri's second year away (2012). I had booked for us to go to a Saturday afternoon matinee. You informed me that it was the FA cup final that afternoon, which you wanted to watch then discuss with Adri. I suggested that you could watch the match after the show, then speak to Adri and you agreed. However, during the show you fainted while edging your way along the row to get out. We had to stop the show and ask for any doctor in the audience to come forward – three came to help. When the paramedics arrived they put you on a stretcher and as they carried you out of the theatre, you looked at the audience and waved, at which everyone clapped. You were taken to hospital where you had a lot of tests but you insisted that you be allowed home to speak to Adri via Skype.

Adri, however, was not a cricket fan so that was one sport you would share only with me. When we first started living together in Maida Vale, we used to go to the local park where, in the summer months, there was often a cricket match being played. We would sit on the side and watch the match, whilst you explained the rules of the game to me. Cricket was a total mystery to me, as we do not play it in Italy. You explained about the skill required in spinning the ball and the meaning of the 'ridiculous' umpires' gestures. I was so in awe of you, of your zest for life, your patience and your desire to share everything with me. In Italy, you introduced the locals to the game with improvised wicket stumps. In the eighties, Ian Botham was the England team's star and he became your hero. At times, you took Adri and his twin friends, Louis and Lance Boyd, to the park to play cricket. And every time you bowled, you said, “Beefy Botham beats Boyds.” You loved a good alliteration. When the Ashes or one day cricket were being played, you used to update me on the team’s progress. Although I knew I was second best, I did not mind listening to your updates. You told me that in your younger days you were quite good at rugby and football but, much as you loved watching it, you were not as good at cricket.

During the night you tried to head butt me again when I nudged you onto the toilet bowl. There is a clear pattern to your behaviour but, unfortunately, even though I know you will react badly, I need to ‘nudge’ you in order to stop you from falling on the floor. I am sure you think I am attacking you when I do that. This morning I had manoeuvred you onto the bowl in the downstairs toilet and left you for a moment to go to the kitchen to throw away some paper, when you started shouting, “Hello. Hello.” I came back and asked,

“Why don't you call me by my name if you need me?”

“I don't know your name,” you replied. On our return to the lounge, Ella Fitzgerald was on the radio and you said, “This is Ella Fitzgerald.” You can remember the name of a singer but you have forgotten your wife's name. The sadness of it all. How can I not cry?

11.20 a.m.: You have been to the toilet four times in the past half an hour, but only once successfully. I am exhausted and my back and right elbow are very sore. I know you are worse off but this is not helping me to feel any better.

12.20 p.m.: You have been calling out for the past twenty minutes but every time I come to ask what you need, you say you don't want me. In the last few minutes, however, you accepted my help in going to the toilet, where you had a big shit. This is my life –'cleaning your arse'.

1.05 p.m.: On waking from a little nap, you opened your eyes and looked at me intensely, saying, "Do you have any love for me?"

"Of course I do, Jim, but at times you are so unkind to me that I react badly."

"I miss you Cath. I miss us"

"I know exactly what you are saying and I would give anything to get 'us' back," I replied, my eyes welling up again.

3.00 p.m.: Over lunch you were in a philosophical mood, talking about death and your fear of it. You speculated whether we are just fodder and whether anything remained of us when we go. We also touched briefly on religion and whether we believe in a superior being. We both admitted we did not and only 'prayed' when it suited us or when we needed help. I then suggested that I should read you some poetry. This is role reversal, as in the past you used to read poems to me. I picked up one of the many poetry books we own and opened it at random. This is the first poem I read out to you: Coat by Vicki Feaver.

> *Sometimes I have wanted to throw you off like*
> *a heavy coat.*
> *Sometimes I have said you would not let me*
> *breathe or move.*
> *But now that I am free to choose light clothes*
> *or none at all I feel the cold and all the time I*
> *think how warm it used to be.*

It is such a poignant poem that I burst into tears halfway through it, as I know that this is exactly how I will feel once you have gone, despite the choking, claustrophobic feeling I sometimes experience.

Saturday 25th July 2020

It has been a reasonably good week with no excesses or emergency situations. What has possibly made it easier, is the fact that you have been confined to the house. Even going outside to the garden seems a step too far at the moment. You are still very unsteady on your legs and walk only for short periods. The carers, together with Adri, have eased my burden and I am better equipped to deal with you now that I am having some breaks. You have become needier than ever and want to be near me all the time. If I want to go into the garden for half an hour it seems like a major trauma to you. As mentioned, I have given you a bell that you can ring when you need me. It goes without saying that the bell rings constantly when I am not near you. You leave me alone only when you are asleep and I must admit that I cannot wait for you to doze off, so that I can get on with something else. This 'needy' stage, however, has made you very affectionate and you hug me and kiss me a lot.

Your wit also occasionally appears through the mist. Yesterday I asked, "How are you feeling?" You replied, smiling,

"I am bright enough to know that I am not bright at all." Earlier today, when we were cuddling I said,

"I want you back. I want my husband back." And you replied,

"I want myself back too."

4.00 p.m.: I have just helped you onto your feet after you dropped to the ground like a sack of potatoes again. The effort to lift you up was superhuman because I did not want to get anyone to help me. In the end, you used your legs' power to stand up. When you awoke from your nap I could see that you were panic stricken again. I struggled to get you to stand up and walk to the dining table. Once sat there you stated that you didn't want your lunch. That was very unusual, as food is still something you enjoy. You always eat well and you love your ice cream and chocolate biscuits. I ate my lunch and you asked for ice cream. I replied, "No lunch, no ice cream." You then ate your lunch and after you'd finished your ice cream you were unable to get off the chair, even with my help. When I eventually got you up and was leading you to the sofa, you flopped to the ground again.

It almost appears as though you choose to fall/sit on the floor but that is ludicrous. Who wants to fall? Whatever the reason, getting you on to your feet once again resulted in pain in my back and elbow. I feel thoroughly fed up, pissed off and slightly depressed.

Friday 14th August 2020

Over the past eighteen months there have been moments when I wished you dead. Now that it is happening, I feel completely lost and desperate. I cannot stop crying and I cannot see a life without you, even if you have become a pale shadow of your old self. I just cannot conceive it. I am not suicidal, just totally disinterested in life and what it may offer without you in it.

I went to Italy from 3rd to 9th August, for a break and to see my family. While I was away, Adri moved back into the house to take care of you. When I left the house at 4.30 a.m. on Monday 3rd August you were awake. We kissed and I asked you to be good for Adri. Later that day Adri sent me a video with you walking in the park, then in the evening when we spoke on the phone you seemed okay. On Wednesday, Adri said you were restless but nothing to worry about. On Friday, Adri reported that you did not have a bad night, but by Saturday morning he was worried. He could not get you into the shower and you could hardly move again. Your behaviour was aggressive and you struggled as normal in the toilet. Adri left you by the sofa to go to the kitchen and you fell and scraped your arm on the wall. Adri called me, very upset, as you would not let him clean the cut on your arm. He added that you had tried to head butt him. That night Adri was really distressed, because he'd had little or no sleep for a week, having listened out for you all through the night. This is easier for me as, being in the same bed, I can sleep when you do, as I hear you when you call me to get up. Adri also said that you didn't want to go up to bed that evening and you wanted to sleep on the armchair downstairs. Eventually, he convinced you to go upstairs and put you into bed. On the Sunday morning, he woke up at 8.00 a.m. and knew that something was wrong, as you had not called him once during the night. He went into our room and found you asleep on your back with your feet hanging out, over the edge of the bed. He tried to wake you up but you did not respond and could not stand up. You then peed in the bed. Adri called an ambulance, as you were displaying the typical symptoms of an infection. The ambulance took you to West Middlesex Hospital just after 11.00 a.m. on Sunday 9th August. It now appears that this may be your last admission to hospital, ever. Adri told the doctors and nurses that you display the same symptoms as these when you have an infection. He added that it could possibly be a urine infection, as this is what you suffered from just two weeks previously. The staff mentioned the heatwave as a possible cause for your collapse. After all, we were in the midst of a heatwave. I came to see you on Monday 10th August, my first day back from Italy. I arrived at 3.00 p.m. as this was visiting hours, under COVID-19 restrictions. You slept most of the time. The heat was unbearable and I spent the whole time fanning you with a small fan I had brought from home. You were in an AMU ward when I first arrived but were moved to the Kew ward in the basement at 6.30 p.m., just before visiting hours were over. I followed you to the new ward and was pleased to see that they had air conditioning there. I asked the doctor what was wrong with you and was told that they were carrying out all the relevant tests as they were not sure. At 3.30 a.m. I received a call saying that you had deteriorated and your oxygen level had dropped significantly. I was by your side at 4.00 a.m. They had moved you back to AMU and put you on a ventilator. The doctor said that you had tried to remove the tube that they put in your stomach to feed you. And they believe this may have caused the drop in oxygen. With the ventilator, your oxygen level was up to 92% - 93%, a totally acceptable level. She also told me that you'd had a small heart attack, as the ECG showed some irregularities, adding that the next couple of days would be crucial. Adri had an appointment at the embassy for Truc's visa and was in London all day. I stayed at the hospital until 7.00 p.m. and, as I left, asked the doctors to call me should anything change because they wouldn't let me stay. You were asleep all the time I was there and I continued to fan you as the heat was oppressive. The next morning, Wednesday, Adri bought an electric fan and together we drove to the hospital to put it by your side, as it was still very hot. We arrived at 10.30 a.m. I saw a nurse and explained what we planned to do. She said that she would put the fan by your side. I asked if I could see you, as you were critical. She went to the ward to speak to a doctor, then came back to say that you were fine and they would set up the fan, so I could not see you until visiting time at 3.00 p.m. I left feeling relieved, obviously. When I returned at 3.00 p.m., however, it was clear that you were not fine. You were still totally out of it and unresponsive. The doctor said they were going to put a tube down your throat to feed you. I said that I did not want you to have a tube down your throat, as this is what made you critical in the first instance. I added that you could eat and drink with no problem at home. They are concerned about aspiration of food in your lungs, of course. I told the doctor that although I want you back, I don't want you to have invasive treatments. I just want you to be pain- and fear-free.

They still do not know what is wrong with you but the heart attack now appears to have been a false alarm. You were unconscious all day and totally unaware of my presence. I left at 7.00 p.m., reminding the doctors to call me should anything change.

Thursday 13th August 2020

Adri and I came into the hospital at 3.00 p.m. You have been moved to a more comfortable ward in Syon 2. You are in a room on your own and still asleep. A doctor asked to see us and told us that you are dying, as you are completely unresponsive. She added that they will stop fluids and antibiotics and just keep you comfortable. Both Adri and I were in shock. We came back to your room and when we spoke to you, you definitely reacted to us. You raised your arm twice when we asked you to and you opened your eyes. We asked the doctors if we could stay with you all the time and we were granted permission. Adri stayed for a while, during which time we both talked to you and told you how much we loved you. I spent Thursday night with you and asked the nurse to continue with antibiotics and fluids. On Friday morning I told the doctor that because you responded to us, we wanted to continue with treatment and start feeding you through a drip. She said that a drip feed was not an option at the moment but they would continue with fluids and antibiotics. She also said that people do respond at the end of their lives sometimes, to say goodbye. But she still believes that you are dying. I was back by your side when your eyes opened for a few minutes. You said 'ciao' to me and 'hello' to the doctor when she came in to feel your poor chest. You also showed some recognition when Adri and Truc Facetimed you on their way to the embassy again. Your chest is making a horrible noise and your breath is really laboured. The doctor reiterated that you are not responding to the treatment at all. During the afternoon, I saw the palliative care nurse and asked her, "How is it possible that my husband is dying, when his heart is okay, his liver is okay, his kidneys are okay and his brain is as okay as it used to be? Only his lungs are bad at the moment."

"It does happen," she said. "It takes only one organ to fail." She told me that we had three options for you:

1) to remain in hospital
2) to go home and be looked after by District Nurses or
3) to go into a hospice.

I told her that the hospice is not an option but, going home, depending on the time required is definitely a possibility.

Adri spent last night with you and said you were out of it almost the entire time. My love, please do not fight it. If it is time to go, just go. Do not suffer unnecessarily. 'Please go gentle into that good night'. You always quoted this poem to me but you were definitely set against going gently and instead 'Rage against the dying of the light'. Please let yourself go, my love. I am not prepared or ready to lose you but I do not want you to suffer.

Saturday 15th August 2020

I am at home, as Adri spent the night with you. I am looking out of the window and there is a DPD van delivering a parcel to our neighbour. I do not understand how the world can continue as if nothing was happening, while you are on your final journey. I had asked Matt to come and look at putting a ramp and rail to help you into the garden, as lately you have been afraid to do the two steps leading outside. We will not need this adjustment now. And the front door, which I had installed to make it easier for you to get in and out and which has caused us so much trouble, is still not working properly.

12.48 p.m.: I arrived at the hospital half an hour ago and Adri said that you had an okay night but added that your chest had been really bad during the evening. You then relaxed and slept. I see that your eyes are full of sleep. I pick up a wipe and clean them. Your breath has become very heavy and you seem to be struggling to breathe. I ask a nurse to give you something to help you breathe more easily. You open your eyes, look at me pleadingly and tears run down your cheek. I kiss your forehead and try to reassure you. "Just relax my love. You sleep and do not worry about anything. The nurse will give you something to help you breathe. Just feel the love around you. I love you so much my love. You sleep and I will stay right here, by your side." Why is it so difficult to die? And how painful will it be for me without you? At the moment I feel I will also stop

breathing when you do, but I know it will not happen and this fills me with both relief and dread at the same time.
4.00 p.m.: You have been asleep for the past two hours and you appear peaceful. You look so gaunt and your cheeks have sunk but your mouth is still beautiful. I remove the oxygen mask and kiss that sensual mouth of yours. I hope you can soon stay asleep for good, without any suffering or fear, my love. Now that we have been told you are dying, I hope it will happen fast without you being aware of it. Death has always been your greatest fear. I met you when you were forty years of age and you were terrified of dying even then. Because your father died at forty-four years of age, when you reached your fourty-fourth birthday you were sure you were going to die as well. Why this should be the case, you could not explain, but you really feared it.

You drank and smoked heavily and, given your family history of heart problems, you also felt that one day you would drop dead as your brother had. This fear was clearly accentuated every time you had chest pains. And there were chest pains and scary moments through the years. Then you were diagnosed with Angina and in 1995, at the age of fifty-six, you had a triple bypass. This was very successful and afterwards you managed to lead an almost normal life with just odd scares here and there. In 2003, you had surgery for bowel cancer and that was another dark period for us. Your fear of death increased, with justification. But you were very strong and you overcame the cancer as well. However, you have always been very aware of your bowel movements and your faeces' consistency from that moment onwards. You had a number of serious health issues over the years but you were a bit of a hypochondriac as well. Any headache, tummy ache or pain anywhere could mean sudden death and you tended to worry and become morose and distant. These worries would then trigger your anxiety and angst. At these times, you saw the world as a very scary place and life could be very black for a few days. I used to stay physically very close to you during these anxious periods, caressing your head, your face and holding your hand. To help you leave this dark hole I talked to you lovingly and soothingly, reminding you of what we have and how lucky we are to have found each other. Eventually, you would manage to pull yourself back up and you would regain your sense of humour and love of life. You loved Spike Milligan's epitaph, 'I told you I was sick'. He was another notorious hypochondriac. I am sure that your love of life was emphasised by this fear of death. Everything you did was bigger, more colourful, brighter and more vibrant, because it was felt more deeply due to the constant presence of death in the background. You often said, "You will have to shoot me, as I seem able to overcome everything." You knew, however, that Parkinson's was not going to go away. You could not overcome this unstoppable terminator. Shielding turned out to be a waste of time for you, as you had your in-built time bomb.

Sunday 16th August 2020

7.53 a.m.: I have just spent the night with you in hospital. You appear comfortable enough but your chest is still bad in spite of the antibiotics. You do not want to give up. You have been without food for more than six days and without fluids for over twenty-six hours now but you keep breathing. I hope you are not in pain and not afraid.

I asked three different nurses, who all said that you would be agitated and grimacing if you were in discomfort. I must believe this. Why is it so difficult to go to sleep for good? Is it your willpower hanging on to life with everything you have left? Are you 'raging against the dying of the light'? You have always held on to life and fought illness like a true warrior. This battle, however, cannot be won. They have told me this and I really wish you could let go of this mortal coil, my love. "Amore, I feel so guilty for the times I have been unkind to you. The times I have been a bully. The times I withdrew my affection. The times I thought your neediness was a nuisance. Amore, I hope you know that in spite of all these times my underlying ever present feeling is love, affection and dedication. I hope you remember the good times my love, and we had many."

5.23 p.m.: They have just topped up your drugs and you didn't stir. You look peaceful and relaxed. Over the past month you had started saying 'I am going to die today'. You would repeat this every three or four days. And every time I would respond, "You are not going to die. You are strong. You have been afraid of dying all your life and you are still here. Mind you, if you keep saying it, it will become a reality one day as we will all die at some point." Was this a premonition, brought on by the many infections that have plagued us for the past few months? I was exchanging text messages with Rachel and she rightly said that I had already started the grieving process when I saw you slipping away from me bit by bit. I do not understand why I feel so totally desolate and cannot stop crying, rather than feel relieved that your suffering will soon be over.

I have been reading some of Leonard Cohen's poems to you, from his 'Book of Longing' and I do hope that you can hear me and get some solace from the reading. You bought this book for me. And there is a dedication in it, signed 'Love Gim'. You would sign your name on some of your dedications with a G, because that is how I spelled your name the first time I wrote a note to you, all those years ago.

8.28 p.m.: The nurses washed you and changed your position three hours ago and you have not moved since. Thinking about it, you have not moved since Thursday, when you raised your arm for Adri and me. You could never stay still. You were always shifting, kicking, turning. My poor, poor love, so lifeless already. Now that I know you are not coming back to me I would rather you flew away.

Wednesday 19th August 2020

8.30 a.m.: And then, on Monday 17th August, between 11.42 and 11.47 a.m. you did fly away, silently, without fuss, as though you did not want to disturb anyone.

That morning, after you'd had a good night's sleep, the nurse checked your vital signs, which were fine. When I put my hand on your chest I could not feel that raspy sound that you had made over the past week. I really thought that you were getting better and I told Adri this when he rang. "Adri, his chest is clear, the oxygen level is good and his pulse is okay."

"Has he moved, Mum?"

"No, but we would not stir either with all these sedatives and drugs. They cut out all nourishment and fluids and I am going to ask them to restart giving him fluids via the drip."

"Yes, talk to the doctor but don't raise your hopes, Mum," he advised. When the doctor arrived at 11.42 a.m. she felt your chest and I told her I thought you were getting better. She was with Abigail, the palliative nurse and another nurse. We went to a separate room and I asked them to reinstate some fluids. The doctor agreed to start a slow drip but warned that it may create problems for your chest again. She also asked me how you had been lately, so I told her that in the past six to eight months you have had infection after infection in your chest and urine. She said that this is typical of Parkinson's and is what kills sufferers in the end, but she agreed to reinstate some fluids. I returned to you exactly five minutes later and knew as soon as I entered the room that you had gone. The colour had drained away from you. I came close and saw that you were not breathing. I called the doctor who was still outside and she confirmed you had gone. I could not believe that you had slipped away in the few minutes you were on your own. Over the past four days either Adri or myself have been by your side constantly, holding your hand, talking to you, playing music or reading poetry, day and night, because we didn't want you to be alone. And you flew away when no one was there with you. The doctor said that this tends to happen quite often. I hope you know my love that you are loved deeply and I will always carry you in my heart. I hope you forgive me for the unkind words and the sheer nastiness I showed at times, but love has always been the constant. I love you my beautiful man. I dreamt about you last night. A happy dream and I know you are okay.

Wednesday 9th September 2020

We are not religious people but we both hoped that there could have been a place where our 'essence' could roam freely and serenely after death, and we used to say that whoever should die first would have to give the other one a sign of their presence. Since you have gone I have seen so many 'signs' that I truly believe you are looking out for me.

- I dreamt about you three or four times already. They are brief but vivid dreams and in all of them you seem happy.
- Just before your funeral, a beautiful butterfly was flying around our living room. It must have been you, as we had never seen a butterfly in our house before.
- Quite often, we were woken up in the morning by collared doves but I had never seen one near home until the other day, when I saw two white doves on the roof opposite our house.
- You used to be surprised every time you looked at the digital clock in our bedroom and saw the same numbers on the display, such as 11:11 or 3:33, and you used to point this out to me. I never paid much attention but over the past few days, on three separate occasions, I have been looking at the clock when the same numbers were displayed.

I love you and have loved you all my life but I regret not having been kind enough to you over the past few months.

When you asked me to hold your hand, I would do so for a while and then would let it go with some excuse or other. How I would love to be able to hold your hand now. I was in Twickenham yesterday, walking by the river as we used to and I saw an inscription on a bench that could have been written by me, for you: 'If love could have saved you, you would have lived forever.' Ciao you!

On the following pages are hand written notes from Jim.

Nothing to say except
I love you more each day
You're all my life
Dai xxx

Missed you today
so bought this
for my love.

x x Gem x x

The Devil's Feather

YOU ARE ALONE MY EVIL AND MY GOOD

WITH YOU I HAVE EVERYTHING –

WITHOUT YOU NOTHING.

JIM XX

Dear Kelli

It just keeps getting better

between us, doesn't it.

Love you.

x Jim.

Keith
Something simple
to introduce you
to the reading habit again
But, My God, I love you
Dri.

as promised
to my constant mistress
with Love
Jim

I might forget the gifts,
but I never forget
I love you.

XX

I repeat,

You'll love this book

Did I tell you I love you

cos I forget.

Luv Me

There are only 5 novels
by Alison Lurie - this is
your second - Hope you enjoy
it as much as the first.
I hope you love me as
much as I love you
Jim

Happy CHRISTMAS

To my favourite ~~Fren~~

Friend

+ Lover

I AM, I AM, I AM

so you are
loved by me

x [illegible]
x x xx

Dear Kelti,

To be without you would be an "unBearabl Heaviness".

Love Jim.

Cathy:
This is Jim's Utopia.
Love.

RUNNING OUT OF WAYS
TO TELL YOU HOW
MUCH I LOVE YOU

Where Are You?

On the following pages are photographs of Jim and Adri, folowed by Jim and I.

Katie Herdman

Katie Herdman

Printed in Great Britain
by Amazon